HAND D

HAND DYNAMICS

A Method for Developing Dexterity, Sensitivity and Psychophysical Balance

By Daim Batangtaris

JAPAN PUBLICATIONS, INC.

Cover drawing and illustrations by George Foster/Professionals, Amsterdam

Published by JAPAN PUBLICATIONS, INC., Tokyo

Distributors:
UNITED STATES: *Kodansha International/USA, Ltd., through Harper & Row, Pub-lishers, Inc., 10 East 53rd Street, New York, New York 10022.* SOUTH AMERICA: *Harper & Row, Publishers, Inc., International Department.* CANADA: *Fitzhenry & Whiteside Ltd., 150 Lesmill Road, Don Mills, Ontario M3B 2T6.* MEXICO AND CENTRAL AMERICA: *HARLA S. A. de C. V., Apartado 30–546, Mexico 4, D. F.* EUROPEAN CONTINENT: *Boxer books, Inc., Limmatstrasse 111, 8031 Zurich.* AUSTRALIA AND NEW ZEALAND: *Book Wise (Australia) Pty. Ltd., 101 Argus Street, Cheltenham Victoria 3192.* THE FAR EAST AND JAPAN: *Japan Publications Trading Co., Ltd., 1–2–1, Sarugaku-cho, Chiyoda-ku, Tokyo 101.*

First edition: August 1983
ISBN 0–87040–532–2

Printed in Hong Kong

Dedicated to everyone who has, directly or indirectly,
contributed to the realization of this project

*Es ist nichts Geistiges, was nicht in den Bereich
der Hand und des Armes fiele.* (Goethe)
(There is none akin to spirit, which does not occur within
the purview of the hand and the arm.)

Preface

One picture may say more than a thousand words. Similarly, one key-experience may clarify more than either a thousand pictures or a million words can. This is why I feel that a holistic (wholeness-oriented) approach to hand development ought to be centered on intuition rather than on theory. Keeping *Hand Dynamics* an open system will allow it to mold itself flexibly to the various interests of those working with it. An equally important reason for avoiding any training concept based on blind obedience is more philosophical. The momentum behind hand development springs from the central source of all life, the very heart of human nature. This all-regulating principle has not just invented the hand-arm system and monitored its construction. It is equally responsible for continuously re-adapting its practical applicability. Therefore, a functional improvement of this system is nothing more (yet certainly nothing less) than the last link in a chain of refinement which is as long as the evolution of humanity itself.

In the past, the cultural institutions to which this "finishing touch" function was assigned only had indirect means for doing so. The stimulation of skill training and the integration into the educational system of subjects like art and handicraft were the only developmental strategies available to them.

Today, with the publication of *Hand Dynamics*, a new alternative has been created. By-passing the unnecessary detours of conventional methods, hand functions can now be cultivated by tapping directly into the body's natural wisdom. Once having learned how to respond adequately to the subtle promptings of what is called the "Collective Unconscious," one will readily become certain about the course one's development has to take.

In an early stage, no doubt, some measure of support can be desirable, or even necessary. If the succint theory section of this book does not meet this need, supplementary reading material is listed in the bibliography.

A possibly more attractive option is to order the wide-ranging cassette collection accompanying this book. Write to:

HAND DYNAMICS INSTITUTE
P. O. Box 65930
2506 EE The Hague
Netherlands

Already available is a complete *Hand Dynamics* workshop series in which the author gives an in-depth commentary on *why* and *how* one should do the various exercises. The Institute is also developing a Special Interest Program featuring well-known speakers on topics like yoga, massage, body language, art, music, dance, handicrafts, physiotherapy, psychotherapy, child development and self-actualization in general. Within this context they will be given ample opportunity to elaborate on hand development as it relates to their particular field of expertise.

I trust that all this will provide us with enough guidance to ensure that the voyage to the unexplored regions within ourselves will ultimately be crowned with success.

SELF-ACTIVITY OPENS THE WAY TO SELF-KNOWLEDGE
SELF-KNOWLEDGE OPENS THE WAY TO SELF-FULFILLMENT

Contents

Introduction

The following chapters touch upon some of the most fundamental facts of hand development. The three main aspects which will recurrently be emphasized are:

1) *Hand Dynamics* develops the human being in its totality.
2) The degree to which we are able to use our hands flexibly has a determining influence on the quality of our lives.
3) "Hand-Power" is an evolutionary force affecting our eco-system and, by extension, nature as a whole.

Hand Development

With the advance of automization, man is gradually becoming emancipated from hard labor.

In pre-technological societies, the use of bare hands for activities such as digging, pulling and lifting was an exasperating, body-draining job. In modern society, the full mechanization of labor appears to have re-channeled the main thrust of energy from the muscular to the nervous system.

This transformation has, of course, both a positive and a negative side: The sudden surplus of comfort has to be paid for with the risk of developing psychophysical degeneration symptoms and feelings of alienation.

Modern problems of this sort can only be countered by instituting preventive health programs . Such programs ought to promote self-actualization on all possible levels because nothing can be more re-vitalizing than the blossoming of latent potentials for growth. Definitely among the most important growth potentials is a complex of faculties referred to as "handiness."

Handiness could best be described as a kinetic variant of non-verbal intelligence (i.e., the ability to co-ordinate outer with inner reality through a language-transcending mode of synthesis). On the physical side, it is determined by such factors as strength, flexibility, speed, endurance and sense of touch. From a psychological point of view, the faculties required are concentration, co-ordination, adaptation, creative improvisation and, naturally, learning in general.

Thus, perfecting manual functions is not just a matter of developing the body. It involves the mind and psyche as well.

The fact that hand development is of great educational value has been recognized by every expert in the field. Montessori made it perfectly clear that: "First, children learn with hands, then with brains." Jaspers had the same thing in mind when he wrote: "Thoughtfully engaging in manual activity is the actual training of thinking itself."

This strong emphasis on the importance of hand development is not at all surprising if we realize that practically every act which we as social beings perform requires some sort of manual skill. Regardless of whether we are working, playing or making love, the use of hands is absolutely essential in most situations of daily life.

The Creative Hand

All through history, creativity has been celebrated as the highest achievement of man. Certainly in our age, it has become the commonly shared ideal of millions. From artist and manager to pupil, housewife and pensioner, each one of us is expected to be as creative as possible.

To give everybody a chance to discover his own inner source of "practical fantasy," many community centers and corporations have started offering courses in creativity training. This is a laudable development, of course. The only regrettable thing about it is that its emphasis is put almost exclusively upon brainstorming, while practical creative action is neglected. Musicians for example, must achieve a high degree of psychophysical self-mastery to be able to translate artistic potential into its musical equivalent. Their thoughts must be here-and-now oriented, their feelings empathetic in nature, their perceptions focused and their movements perfectly under control. Only then they may rightfully expect their work to bear the hallmark of excellence.

In other words, it is inner subtlety combined with outer micro-precision that determines the ultimate quality of a musical performance.

The actual outpouring of such creative acts is channeled by the body, especially the hand-arm system. If the channel is blocked, creativity is blocked. Consequently, just like elaborate hi-fi equipment, the body requires expert handling, proper tuning and regular maintenance. That is in fact one of the main facets of *Hand Dynamics*. It is designed to help perfect the capacity for creative self-expression.

The Sensitive Hand

Try the following experiment. Take a baby is your arms and observe what is happening to your body, mind and psyche. All of a sudden, movements become subtle, thoughts lovely, feelings tender. Put the baby down and lift up a sack of potatoes instead. In no time, all subtleness, loveliness and tenderness will have vanished.

What is the lesson we can learn from this experience? Obviously, the physical sense of touch is only one of many determinants of sensitivity. More important and at the same time more susceptible to development is what is generally referred to as an "attitude towards life." For example, if you are emotionally "tight," your gestures will be somewhat stiff and claw-like in appearance. Conversely, once you allow yourself to be open and spontaneous, your entire body will be graced with flexibility, sensitivity and warmth.

As you see, it is our attitudes, which predispose the way we perceive and experience the world. Those who choose for strength and power will have to conform to the stress-inducing demands on which these values are based. The better alternative, of course, is to become gentle and loving because this will attune you almost automatically to life's harmony principle. Having grown beyond conflict, you will find that the most subtle level of sensitivity is positively related to the degree to which one can "accept things as they are." What's more, I see no real difference between insensitivity and the self-encapsulating attitude of being overly defensive. We armor ourselves against what we deem to be a hostile environment lest our "vulnerable soul" be trampled down. But instead of trying to repel trouble by becoming tense, we may as easily become so transparent as to let it pass by.

The main advantage of such a "transparent" attitiude is the synergic equilibrium it helps to establish. Train yourself to be evenminded and you will discover that streaming along freely with the pathways of bio-energy is, indeed, the most natural formula for developing sensitivity.

The Expressive Hand

The hand is the most articulate "speaker" of body language. No part of the body is so expressive as this "organ of organs" (Aristotle) with its unequaled freedom of action. It is the interpreter of spirit, the messenger of the heart, the medium through which the world of ideas reveals its plan of evolution. It is mainly the subconscious mind that "has its say" by means of body language. This it does independent of ego-consciousness, which is why

HANDS REVEAL WHAT TONGUES CONCEAL (see "*The Hand Book*").

In earlier times, this relationship between verbal and non-verbal communication seems to have been much less split. What is more, in all ancient cultures, both spoken language and sign language were employed simultaneously (the American Indian is the best known example of this). Thus, we have reason to assume that the capacities for verbalization and gesticulation are structurally intertwined in a "Siamese twin" type of relationship. Equally suggestive of common roots is the fact that the brain's speech center and hand center are located adjacent to each other. Recent research on speech development has proven that a hand-related psychophysical principle must somehow be involved in the learning process. To quote Mariela Kolzowa: "As long as the fingers are unable to move freely, speech can not develop. . . . The most remarkable thing about this is not that the movements of fingers can influence speech development, but the fact, that up till now we failed to make use of this." (see "*Untersuchungen zur Sprachentwicklung*" in the magazine *Der Kinderarzt* 1975/76).

Let me take this one step further. Is it not logically possible that the use of sign language was already highly advanced when spoken language was still in an early stage of development? This likelihood becomes even greater if we take into account that, psychogenetically speaking, "thinking in images" precedes "thinking in words."

I believe, therefore, that the syntactic depth-structure of spoken language is actually a ramification of the depth-structure of sign language, which itself is but a ramification of the instinctive co-ordinating network underlying body language.

Whether or not this theory will ever be verified is not of primary importance. What counts is the realization that the hand is a channel of life's primeval urge to communicate.

Hand-Brain Relations

Hands and brains represent two complementary aspects of organic self-government. That is to say, brains are endowed with "legislative power." They provide the blueprints for behavior, the basic strategies of action.

Hands are endowed with "executive power." They are infinitely versatile and thus exceptionally capable of translating man's aspirations into tangible reality.

The stupendous intricacy of this interrelationship is, no doubt, life's greatest masterpiece. This hand-brain collaboration has been the prerequisite for man's decisive step from an animal-like being to a "god-like" being. Man was animal-like when he had no choice but to adapt himself to the whimful conditions of his environment. Man became "god-like" when he started to adapt the environment to his own creative will.

We may illustrate this by taking the dolphin as an example. From an evolutionary point of view, his brain development and social communication system is more or less on the same level as that of man. Yet he lacks the organic instrument with which to build a star-traveling civilization.

This clearly shows that intelligence is one thing, its application in real life another. It requires a combination of both to transform natural creatures into "co-creators of Creation." Man acquired this special status by his unique capacity to translate "grasp" into "grip."

We may now better understand what the philosopher Kant was hinting at when he wrote: "Hands are the outside brains of Man." It took science many decades of meticulous research to verify his intuitive findings: the hand center is proven to take up almost one third of the motor brain. The conclusion to be drawn is that these two organs are the most closely interconnected of all.

They are each other's mirror, a unity in diversity. Their inner dialogue generates a continuously amplifying echo, their exchange of catalysts gives momentum to an ever faster swinging pendulum.

Physically, this feedback process is patterned in the shape of a diagonal cross: the left, predominantly verbal hemisphere of the brain has developed its specific traits in the right hand, while the right, predominantly imaginative hemisphere has cultivated its own peculiar characteristics in the left hand.

Consequently, the right hand is superior to the left hand with regard to strength and co-ordination, while the left hand is superior to the right hand with regard to sensitivity and subtlety (in left-handed people, this constellation is usually reversed).

Yet one should not picture this as a one-way, master-slave relationship. Through Hand-Dynamic bodywork, the brain's functioning can undergo the most radical changes (see Exercise 3 of Hand-brain feedback). That is to say, hand development furthers brain development, brain development furthers hand development.

Paranormal Hand Functions

Extraordinary, extra-sensory, not material but energetic—with these connotations in mind, I use the word "paranormal" to indicate that part of the
hand's ability range, which, although less known, is of as much practical
value as "handiness" in general.

"Hand Reflexology" is an excellent example of this. "There is a healing
energy that circulates through the body on specific pathways which were
mapped out centuries ago by man. This energv we call 'life force' or 'vital
energy.' Although this force can be 'tapped' at more than 800 points, Hand
Reflexology shows you how to tap this healing current to bring natural and
prompt relief from practically all your aches and pains, chronic or acute, by
the simple process of massaging the 'reflex buttons' located in your hands.
These 'reflex buttons' are connected to all your glands, organs and the nervous
system.

Reflex massage can not only cure specific ailments but can also be used to
keep you in good health and build resistance to disease. In addition, this
method detects health problems before they become serious. You will gain
more youthful energy, and learn how to reduce health-destroying mental
and physical tensions" (see "Hand Reflexology").

Another interesting hand-related potential is to create so-called "breathing
spaces." In the words of Professor Ilse Middendorf: "The hands are extremely important in breath therapy. We have already seen the effect they
have on various areas of the body through pressure applied by the fingertips.
Our hands mirror ourselves; we stretch them when we breathe in, relax them
when we breathe out. In the motions of our breathing, they can express
everything we potentially are. Through them, we can direct the strength of
our breathing toward ourselves or toward others. They are infinitely expressive, can stimulate or calm, and are essential to movement through breathing"
(see "Your Body Works").

The relationship between the occult element "Air" and the mystery of
how and why the hands function has been equally stressed by the ancient
teachers of yoga science. The hands were considered to be instruments of the
"heart chakra," the energy center which intermediates between the three lower
and the three higher ones. The element dominating its "etheric" metabolism
is said to be "Air," for the "heart chakra" is as much a vehicle for "inter-
centric" communication as the air is a vehicle for voice communication with
the outside world. The synthesizing quality of the heart is, according to the
same teaching, most clearly manifested in the fivefold "wiring" of the hand
(thumb=Ether, forefinger=Air, middle finger=Fire, ring-finger=Water,
little finger=Earth).

Parapsychology is presently trying to translate such subjectively arrived
at knowlege into a model of reality which can be objectively verified. This
pioneering science has produced reliable test material relating to paranormal
hand functions such as:

- "seeing" through one's palms and fingertips
- healing through transfer of bio-energy
- the use of a dowsing rod for locating subterranean water and/or minerals
- the use of a pendulum to facilitate the manifestation of intuitive knowledge
- the materialization of objects (for example, Sai Baba, modern India's most popular guru, who is daily giving evidence of his miraculous powers in public and on TV).

On a more modest scale, yet in no way less miraculous, each of us is a channel of "cosmic energy." Everyone, if he only knows how, can put the "plug" of his physical body into the "socket" of metaphysical reality.

Hand-Power

Tracing the hand's history of evolution all the way back to its origin, one discovers an awe-inspiring wealth of developmental factors, all of which were equally important for the bringing into existence of this "universal tool." The possible purpose of this large-scale development process is relatively easy to understand. The organism externalizes its potential for action in order to gain more freedom and a higher quality of life. If we venture beyond this and start asking questions such as "how, where and when" we plung into a whirlpool of interconnections which utterly transcends human logic.

Nevertheless, we should at least make a serious attempt to expand our consciousness to the point where we can intuit the truth. For in such a state of maximum receptivity, the impression of the hand's mere physicalness gives way to a vision of life's organizing principle of which it is a manifestation. This mysterious capacity for giving direction is an inherent quality in all co-ordinated processes fundamental to nature. Nowhere does this steering force express itself more clearly than in the hierarchical stratification of our own inner being: the mind directs by means of will power, the psyche by means of desire, the body by means of instinct.

Interestingly enough, in relation to man's planetary eco-system, the hand has a similar, yet in this case external organizing function. We may gather from this that the human hand is in fact a central steering factor in the universal transformation process of life's self-unfolding. In a way, it adds the "finishing touch" to Mother Nature's work of art.

In other words, through the intelligent use of this all-round organ, man learned how to domesticate plants and animals, how to build houses, villages and cities, how to manufacture computers, robots and spaceships. In fact, every "thing" devised by man is a direct or indirect legacy of "hand-power."

No doubt, "hand-power" is what made man gain dominion over "all creatures of the earth." Bear in mind: the hand can create and preserve, as well as destroy. Could a magician ever wish for a more ideal "wand"? Can not man, indeed, be likened to a "magician's apprentice" who is holding an instrument of power "in his hand" which he must learn to control lest the invoked forces get "out of hand"?!

In short, having hands means having power, a power which originally did not extend beyond the reach of our arms, but that through gradual development of tools and technology came to encompass the entire globe. Having hands, therefore, means having responsibility as well, a moral responsibility for all we do and choose not to do, including the ultimate consequences entailed.

HAND DYNAMICS
EXERCISES

Preparatory Notes

Concentration

Achieving optimum results requires a heightened state of concentration. If, for instance, you feel like combining practice with activities such as watching TV or listening to records, you should nevertheless keep your attention primarily focused upon what is happening inside of you. You should make sure that those parts of the body which are not directly called upon for exercise are kept relaxed.

Another basic rule to remember is to allow your breathing to become continuously deeper, more flowing, more attuned to inner peace.

Caution

BE CAREFUL NOT TO FORCE ANYTHING. If you feel the least bit of pain, stop practicing right away.

Especially in the earliest stage of development, it is wise to keep training periods short (this applies, above all, to condition and co-ordination training).

Optimum training strategy

1. Start with à short "warming up" period (see description below).
2. Depending upon the degree of difficulty, a self-selected (yet well-balanced) series of exercises may take as long as 15, 30, 45 or even 60 minutes.
3. Pause in between exercises to become aware of (and feel at home in) whatever there is to be experienced.
4. Conclude each training period with 10 minutes (or longer) of TOTAL RELAXATION.

Warm yourself up by vigorous rubbing of:
   a. The fingers
   b. The arms
   c. The backs of both hands
   d. The lower arms
   e. The upper arms including the shoulders

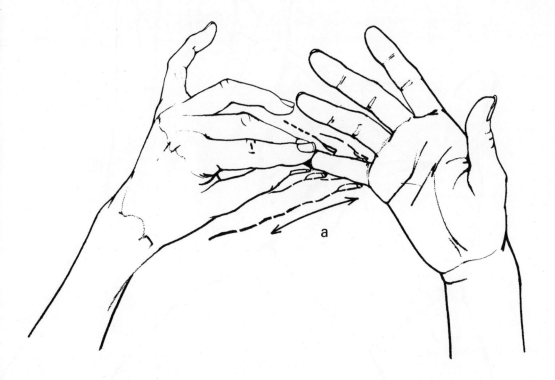

a

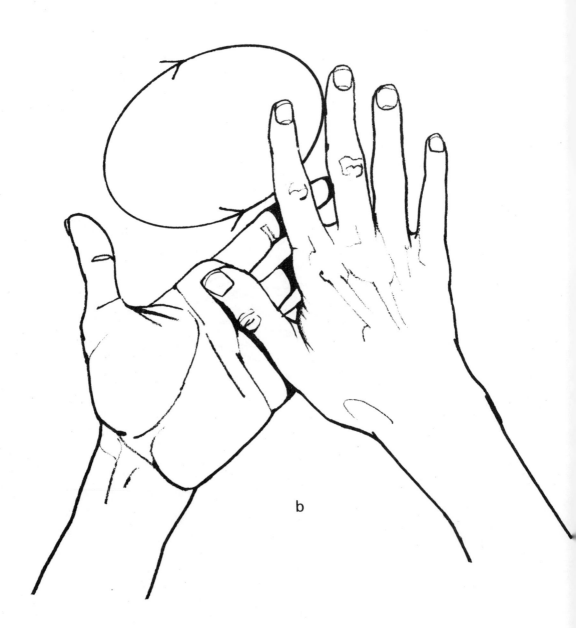

b

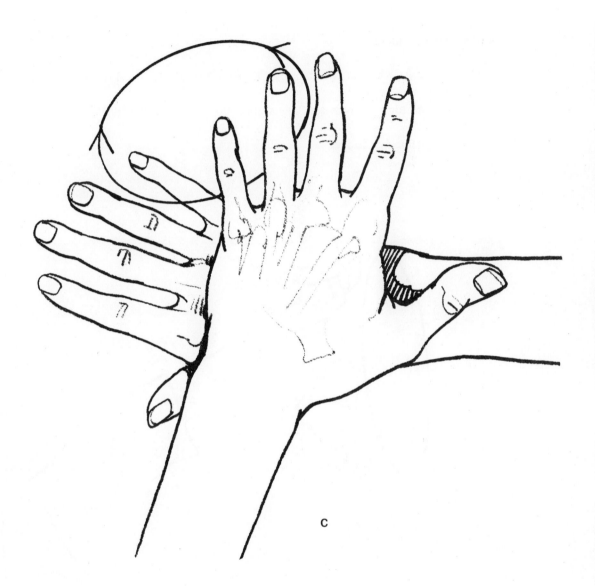

C

Condition Training—Hands

Condition training—hands 1

  a. Forward wrist rotation (wrists loose, hands relaxed) Duration: 20 sec or longer

  b. While continuing the rotation, arms glide slowly into horizontal position
     duration: 15 sec or longer

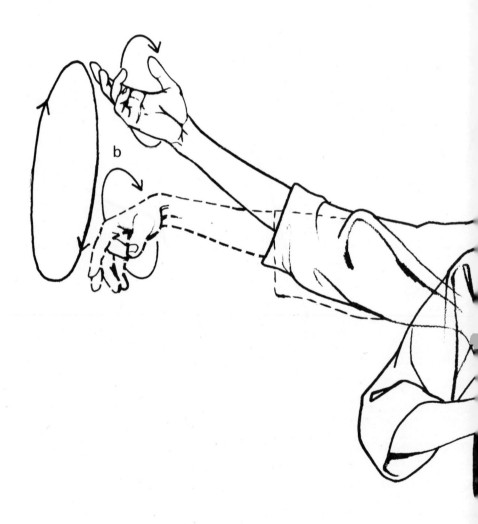

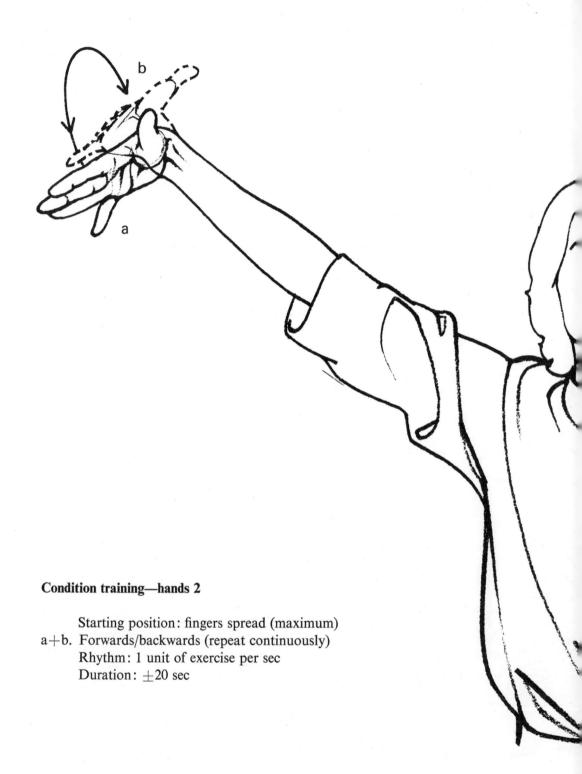

Condition training—hands 2

    Starting position: fingers spread (maximum)

a+b. Forwards/backwards (repeat continuously)

    Rhythm: 1 unit of exercise per sec

    Duration: ±20 sec

Condition training—hands 3

   a.   Starting position: (through soft pressure of left index finger) small finger of right hand pointing up
       Bending/stretching (repeat continuously)

b–d. The same with the ring, the middle and the index finger

e–h. The same with the small, the ring, the middle and the index finger of the left hand
       Rhythm: 1 sec per once bending/stretching
       Duration: ± 10 sec per finger

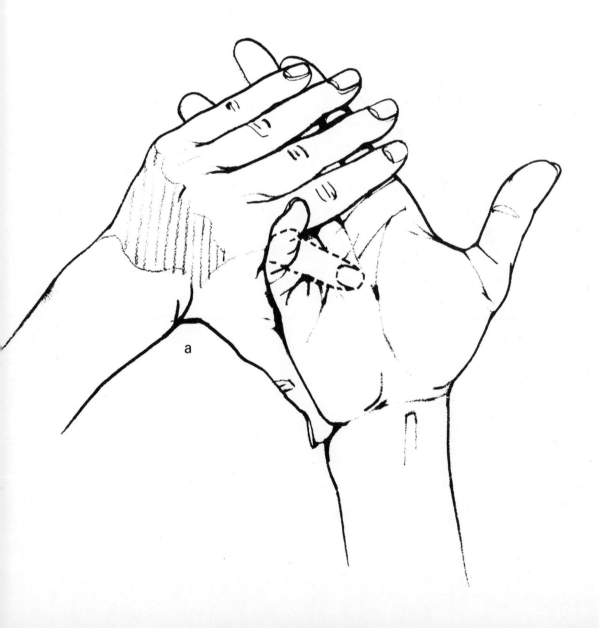

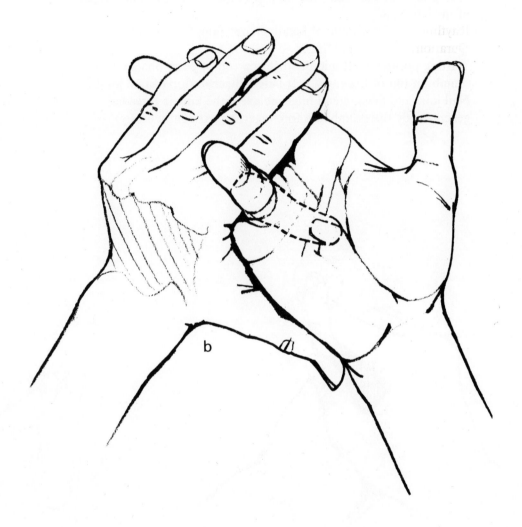

Condition training—hands 4

    a.   Starting position: small finger of right hand stretched, left index finger below nail joint, left thumb above palm joint
         Nail phalanx bending/stretching (repeat continuously)

b–d. The same with the ring, the middle and the index finger

e–h. The same with the small, the ring, the middle and the index finger of the left hand
         Rhythm: 1 sec per cycle of bending/stretching
         Duration: ±10 sec per finger

    i.   Starting position: left middle finger on top of palm phalanx, left thumb on top of finger tip, left index finger on top of nail joint
         Nail joint up/down (small finger relaxed, the kinetic force is generated by the thumb and forefinger, repeat continuously)

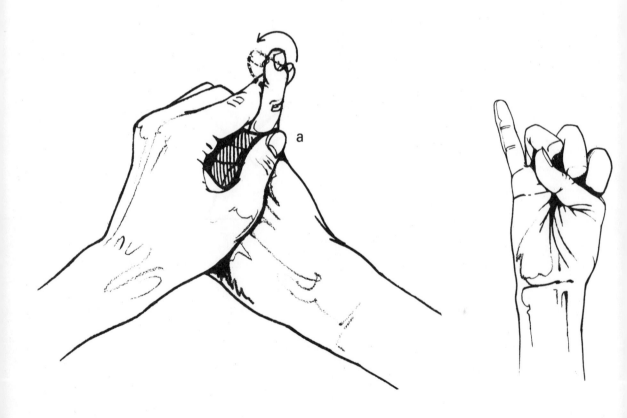

a

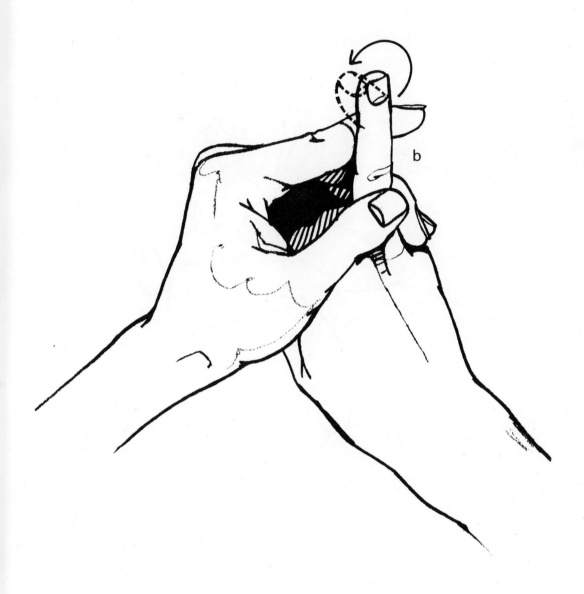

j–l. The same with the ring, the middle and the index finger

m. Starting position: tip of right thumb between thumb and index finger of the left hand
Nail joint up/down (repeat continuously)

n. Folded right thumb between thumb and index finger of the left hand, rotate

o–t. The same as in i–n with the fingers and the thumb of the left hand
Duration: ±10 sec per finger

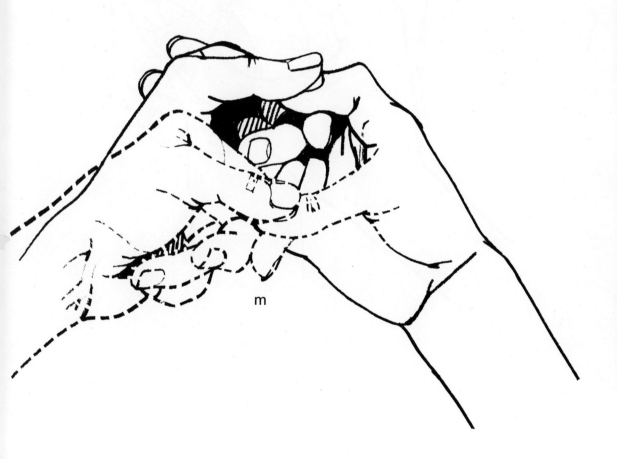

m

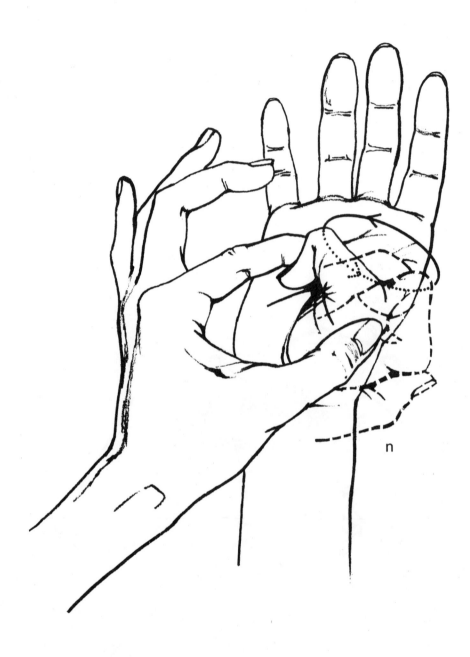

Condition training—hands 5

Starting position: fingers stretched, ring and middle fingers spread
a. Thumbs in outward position, nail joints bending/stretching (once)
b. Thumbs in inward position, nail joints bending/stretching (once)
Rhythm: repeat a+b continuously
Tempo: comfortable
Duration: ±20 sec
c+d. Similar procedure, thumbs up/down

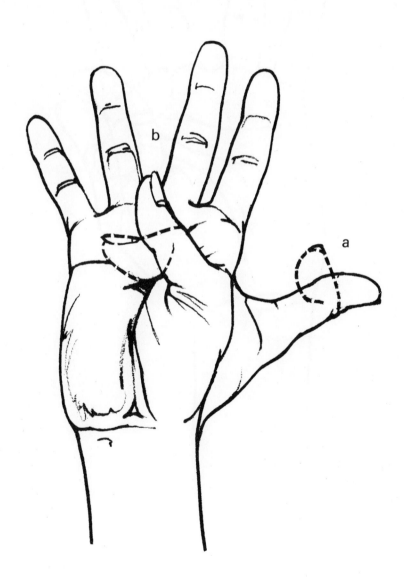

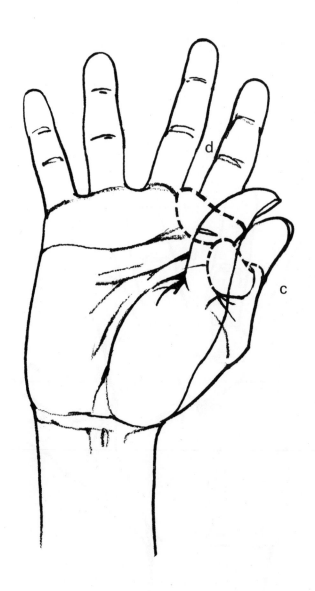

Condition training—hands 6

a–d. Finger rotation in both directions (from palm joint)
e–h. The same with the left hand
    Tempo: comfortable
    Duration: ±20 sec per finger (10 sec per direction)

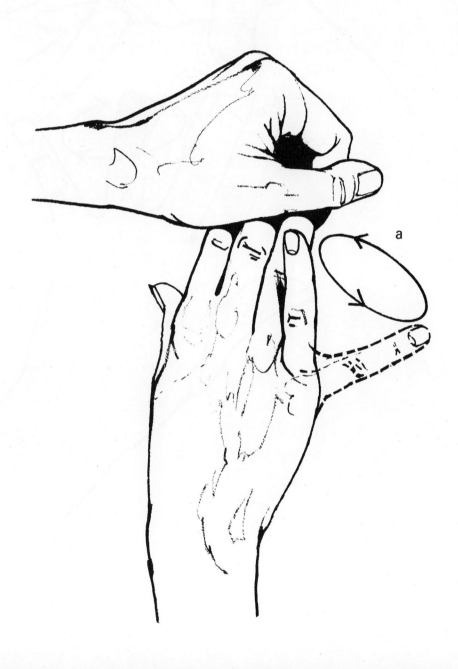

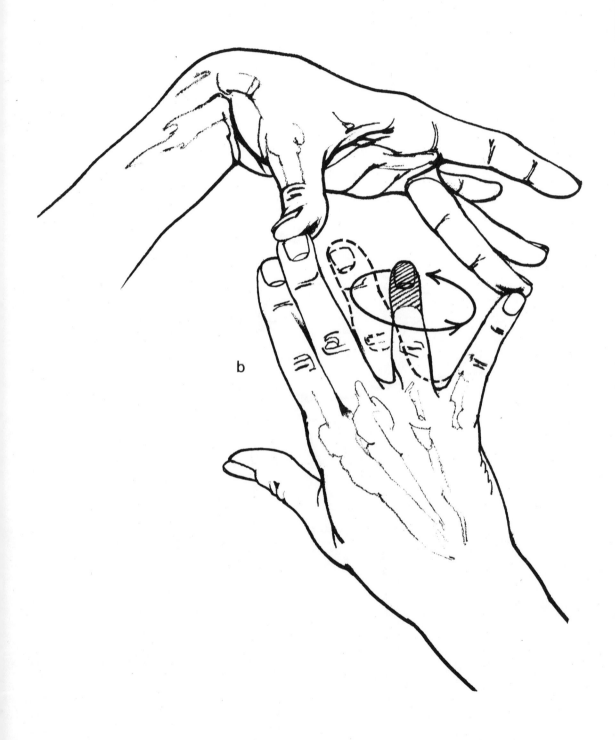

b

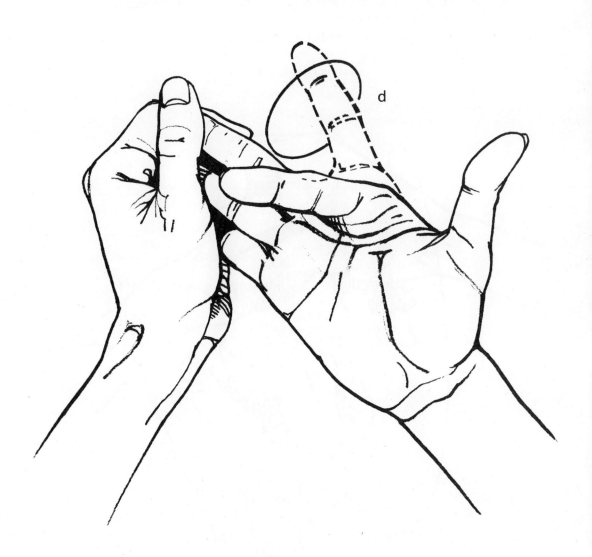

Condition training—hands 7

Starting position: thumb and small finger of the right hand pointing up, thumb and small finger of the left hand pointing down, hands clasp each other

a. Rotate right wrist in both directions (ring, middle and index finger close to the wrist, right hand relaxed)

b. Move ring, middle and index finger to the middle of the back of the hand, resume rotation

c+d. The same with the left hand

Tempo: comfortable

Duration: ±10 sec per direction of rotation

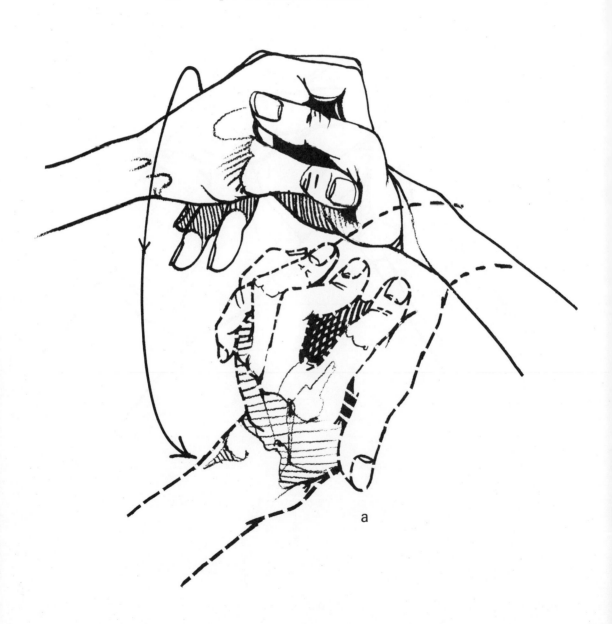

a

Condition training—hands 8

Starting position: arms spread, hands make a fist (nail joints rest upon the thumb)
a. Wrist rotation (in both directions)
b. Figure 8 wrist motion (in both directions)
c. Turning pulled up hands back and forth (in rapid tempo)
   Duration: ±10 sec

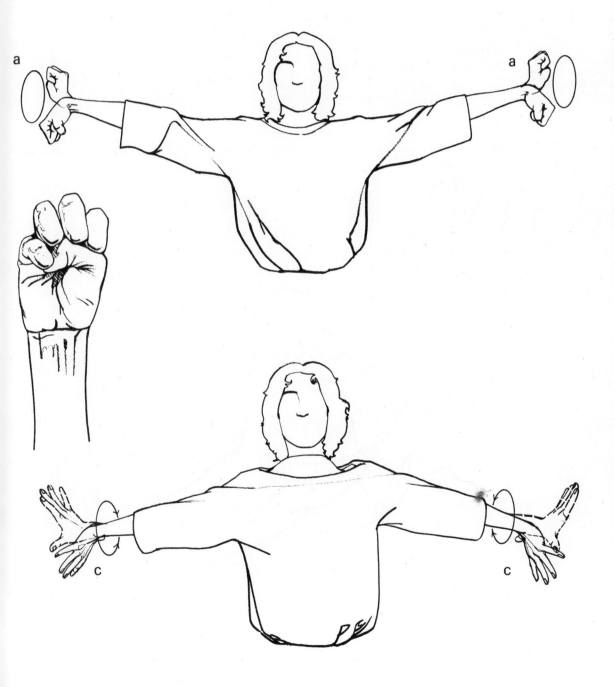

Condition training—hands 9

a+b. Bending/stretching (both the right and the left hand, repeat
     continuously)
     Tempo: fast
     Duration: ±15 sec
 c–h. Fluent transition to wave motion
     Tempo: comfortable
     Duration: ±15 sec
     Then, c-d-e-f-e-d, etc., fingers undulate back and forth
     Tempo: comfortable
     Duration: ±15 sec
     Back to c–h, then a+b

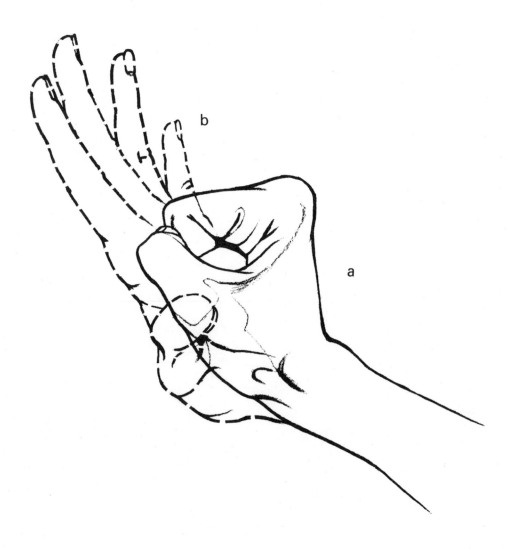

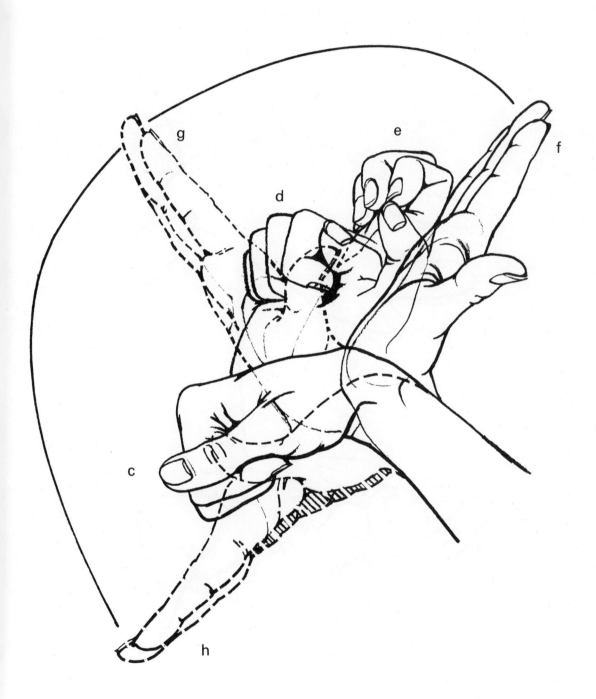

Condition training—hands 10

a. Wave motion generated by the nail joints
b. Transition to wave motion generated by the middle joints

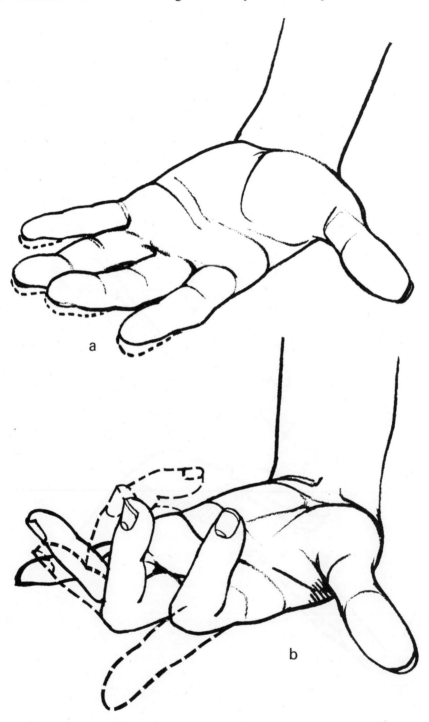

c. Transition to wave motion generated by the palm joints
    Tempo:fast
    Then, d-e-f-g-h-i-h-g-f-e, etc., transition to figure 8 wave motion
    generated by the wrist joints

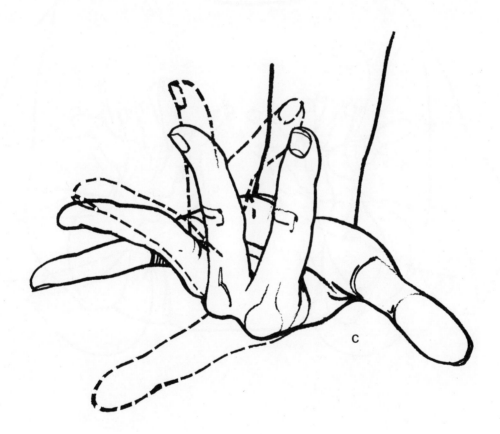

c

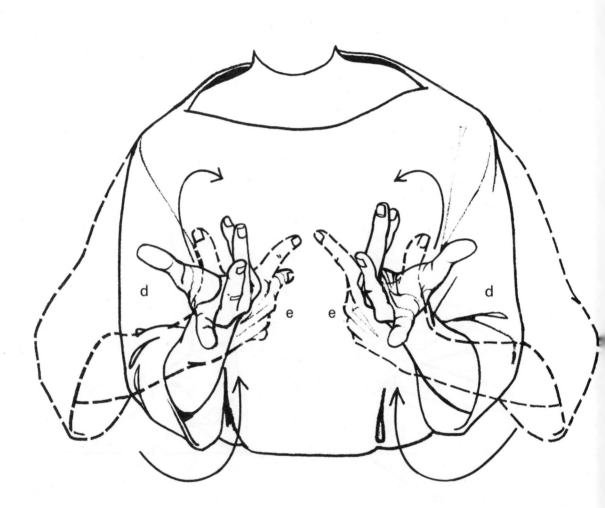

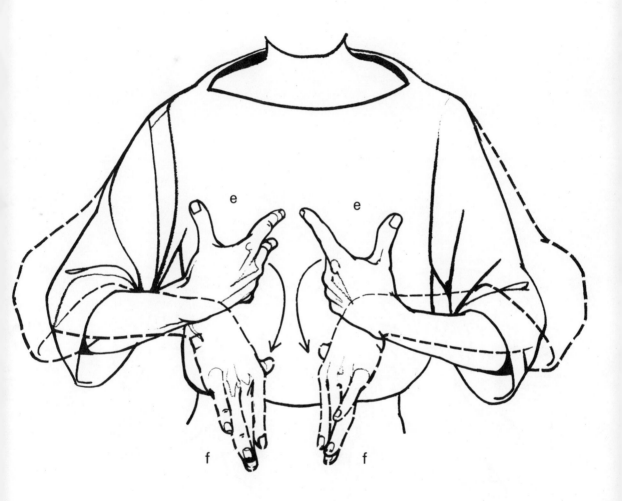

j. Figure 8 motion continued while the arms draw a circle
Tempo: figure 8 motion fast, circle slow
Back to d-e-f-g-h-i-h-g-f-e, etc., then c, then b, then a
Duration: unlimited
Important: let the thumb wave along harmoniously; if in a the nail
joints don't really move, continue to concentrate upon the finger tips

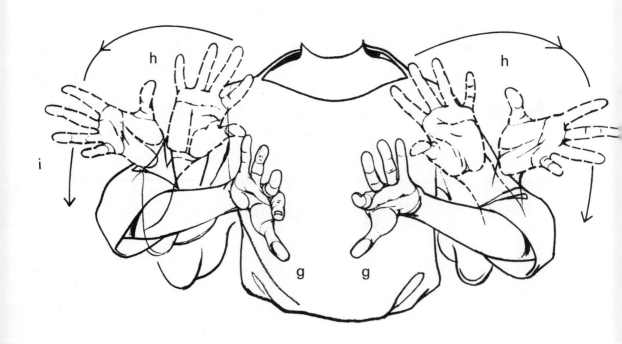

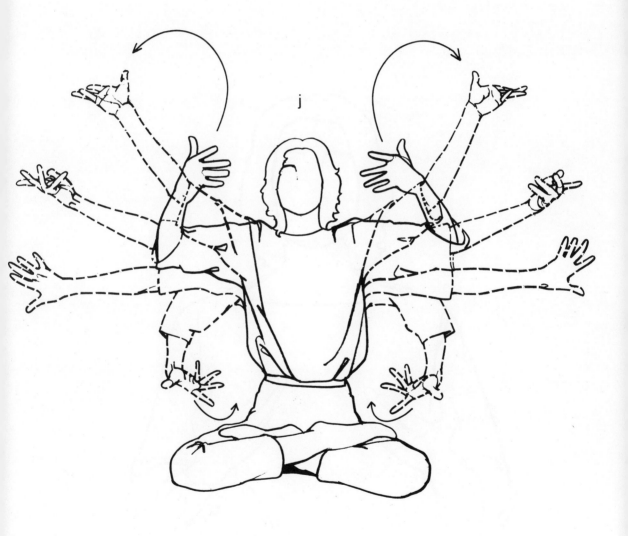

j

Condition training—hands 11

a. Downward "swishing motion" of relaxed hands (repeat continuously)
b. Upwards/downwards (repeat continuously)
   Rhythm: twice per sec
   Duration: ±15 sec

b

c.   Downward "swishing motion" (along both sides of the body, once)
d.   Right hand forwards, left hand backwards (once)
e.   Repeat c
f.   Left hand forwards, right hand backwards (once)
     Then, c-e-f, repeat continuously
     Rhythm: twice per sec
     Duration: ±30 sec
     Back·to b, then to a
     Important: the hands
     should swish like a whip
     (to accomplish this both
     wrists and fingers must
     be kept relaxed)

c+e

f

d

f

c+e

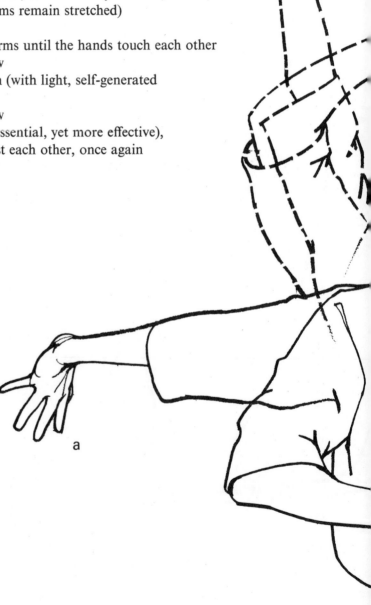

Condition training—hands 12

a. Arms horizontal, fingers spread (small fingers pointing up,
   thumbs pointing down)
   Inhale deeply, hold breath, tense all body muscles, exhale,
   relax body muscles (arms remain stretched)
   Altogether: 3 times
b. Raise the (stretched) arms until the hands touch each other
   Tempo: extremely slow
c. "Pull" the hands down (with light, self-generated
   counter pressure)
   Tempo: extremely slow
d. Nail joints bend (not essential, yet more effective),
   press the hands against each other, once again
   tense all body muscles
e. Total relaxation

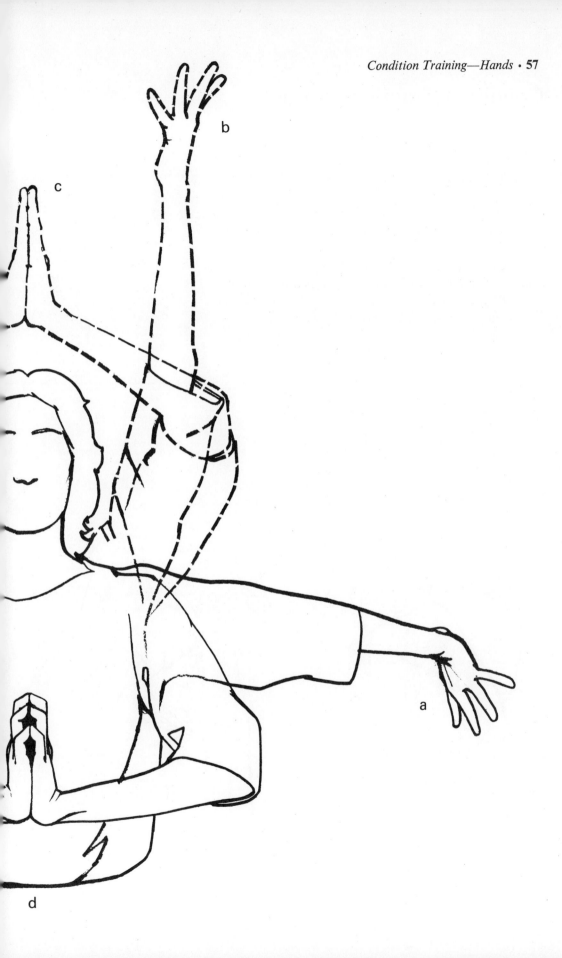

Condition Training—Arms

Condition training—arms 1

a. Shoulder rotation, backwards (fingers rest upon shoulder joint)
b. Shoulder rotation, forwards (with pulled-up palms)
   Tempo: comfortable
   Duration: ± 10 sec per direction of movement
c. "Pendulum" movement (with pulled-up palms)
   Rhythm: once up/down per sec (or slightly faster)
   Duration: ± 20 sec

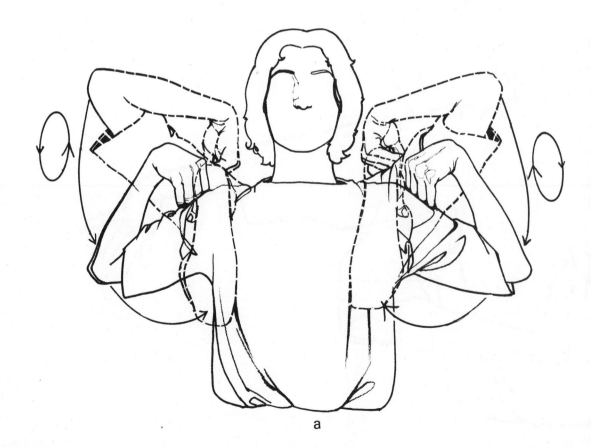

a

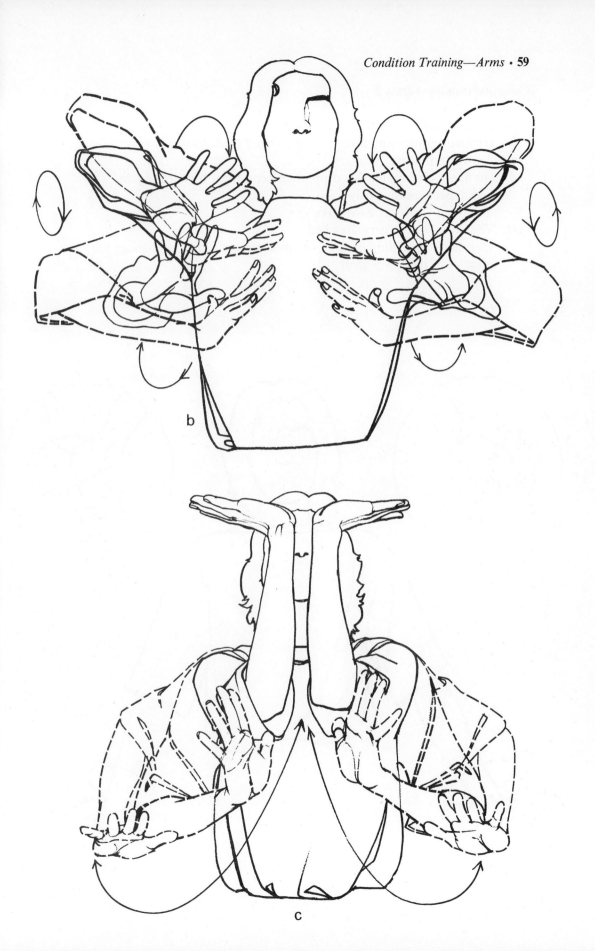

b

c

Condition training—arms 2

    a. Bend forwards, turn fists outward

    b. (In final position) let fists drop, then bend them forwards again

    c. Turn fists inward

    d. (In final position) let fists drop, then bend them forwards again

        a–d, repeat continuously

        Tempo: a+b 1 sec, c+d 1 sec

e–h. The same with fingers stretched

        Duration: depending on level of advancement (don't over-strain the muscles of the lower arm)

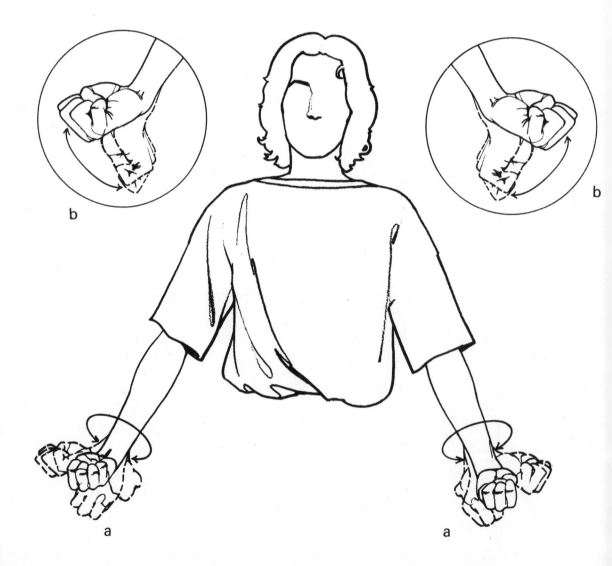

Condition training—arms 3

a. Starting position: arms stretched as far backwards as possible (hands in line with the navel); little fingers up, thumbs down
    Engage both hands in a left/right, pendulum-like motion; repeat continuously
b. Starting position: turn hands 360° (thumbs up)
    Engage hands in pendulum-like motion, repeat continuously

c. Starting position: arms stretched as far backwards as possible (hands far above the head), hand position like in a
Engage hands in a pendulum-like motion, repeat continuously

d. Starting position: hands turn 360°
Hands left/right, repeat continuously
Tempo: once left/right per sec
Duration: ±10 sec per unit of exercise

c

d

Condition training—arms 4

a. "Swish" arms upwards (hands open)
b. While arms "swish" downwards, hands make a fist
c. "Swish" arms downwards (hands open)
d. While arms "swish" upwards, hands make a fist
    Again, a–d, repeat continuously
    Tempo: from slow to maximum speed
    Duration: ±20 sec

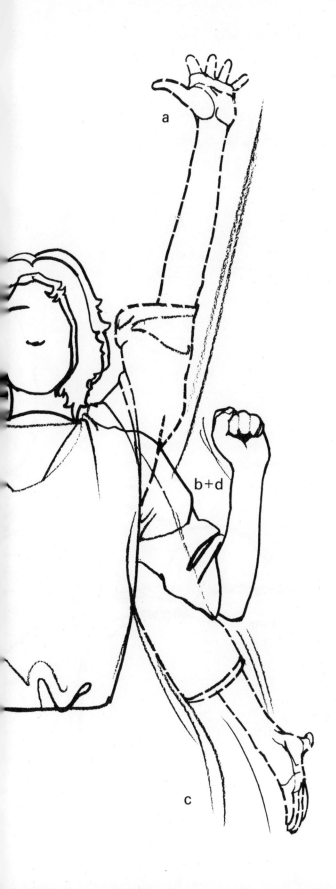

e. "Swish" arms outwards (horizontal, hands open)
f. While arms "swish" inwards, hands make a fist
g. "Swish" arms inwards (right above left arm, hands open)
h. While arms "swish" outwards, hands make a fist
i. "Swish" arms outwards (hands open)
j. While arms "swish" inwards, hands make a fist
k. "Swish" arms inwards (left above right arm, hands open)
l. While arms "swish " outwards, hands make a fist
Again, e–l, repeat continuously
Tempo: from slow to maximum speed
Duration: ±30 sec

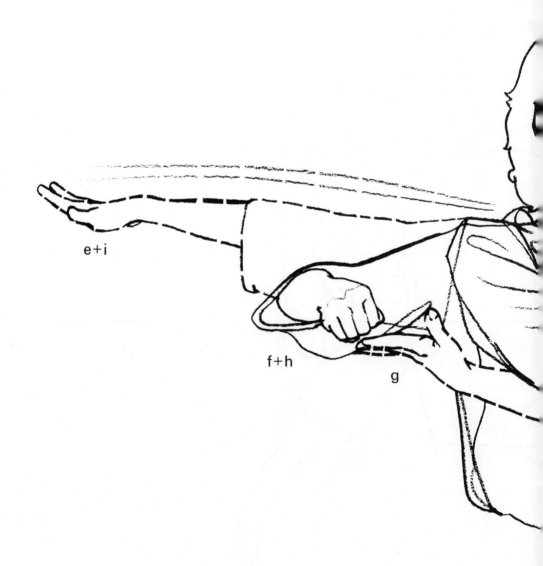

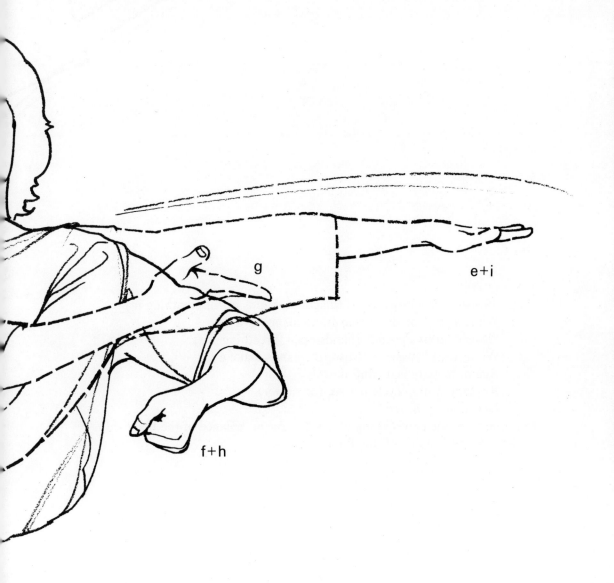

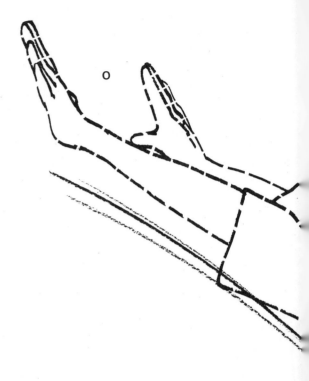

m. "Swish" arms downwards (diagonal, hands open, breathing in)
n. While arms "swish" upwards, hands make a fist
o. "Swish" arms upwards (hands open, breathing out)
p. While arms "swish" downwards, hands make a fist
   Again, m–p, repeat continuously
   Rhythm: 1 m–p cycle per sec (or slower)
   Duration: ±20 sec
Important: let the pelvis swing along; in unit m, balance of the body shifts
to the toes (heels come off the floor)

Condition training—arms 5

Starting position: upper arms horizontal, lower arms and hands relaxed
a. Parallel rotation of lower arms (the kinetic force is generated by the shoulders and the upper arms only)

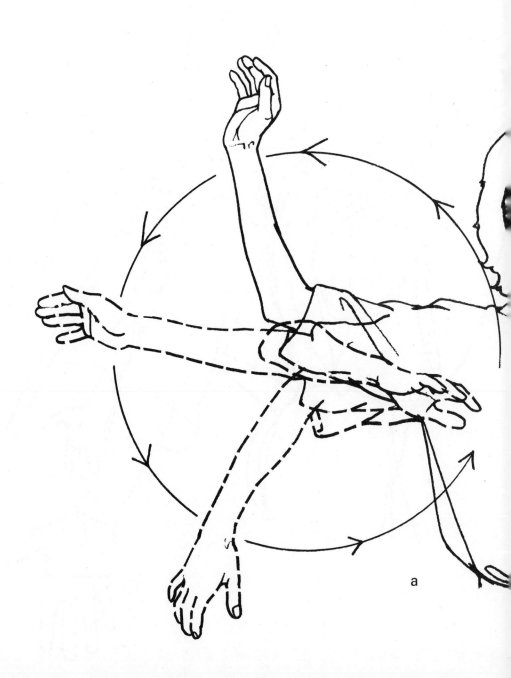

a

b. Non-parallel rotation of lower arms (one lower arm up, the other down)
Tempo: from slow to fast, then back to slow
Duration: ± 20 sec per unit of exercise
Important: lower arms should hang from elbow joints like "ropes"

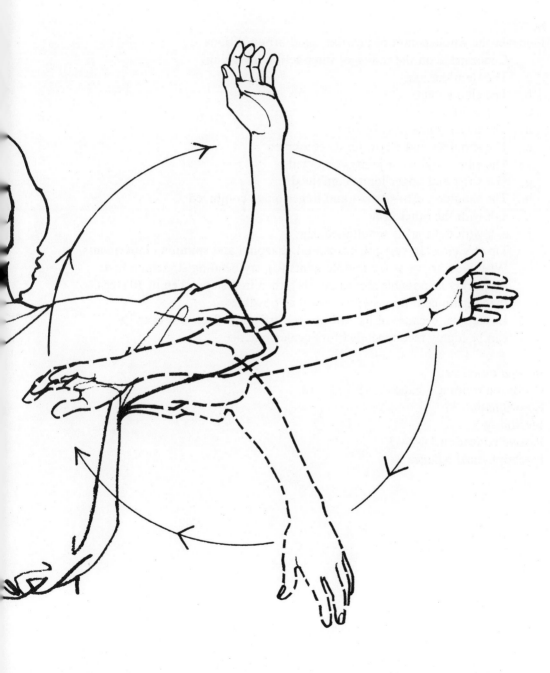

Condition training—arms 6

    a. Forward arm rotation (the kinetic force is generated by the shoulders only)
        Tempo: from slow to fast, then back to slow

        Important: arms should hang from shoulder joints like "ropes"
        Variation: (at top speed) slowly bend your whole upper body forwards and upwards again

NOTES:
Discover the whole gamut of possible hand-arm positions . . .
        Concentrate on the radius of inter-action involving:
    a. The shoulder joint
    b. The elbow joint
    c. The wrist joint
    d. The finger joints (one by one)
    e. The shoulder and elbow joints combined
    f. The elbow and wrist joints combined
    g. The wrist and finger joints combined
    h. The shoulder, elbow, wrist and finger joints combined
    i. a–h with the other arm
    j. a–h with both arms simultaneously
        Tip: try circular, vertical, horizontal, diagonal and spiralling movements
        When you arrive at the middle joints (d), try bending/stretching first
        as quickly as possible (continuously), then in 5 steps, then in 10 steps,
        then (again continuously) as slowly as possible
        Important: because of its "all-in-one" training effect, this exercise
        can be highly recommended for regular practice

Related exercises:
Condition training—hands 2+8+11+12
Co-ordination 12
Flexibility 1
Passive relaxation 1+2+3
Psychophysical balance 2

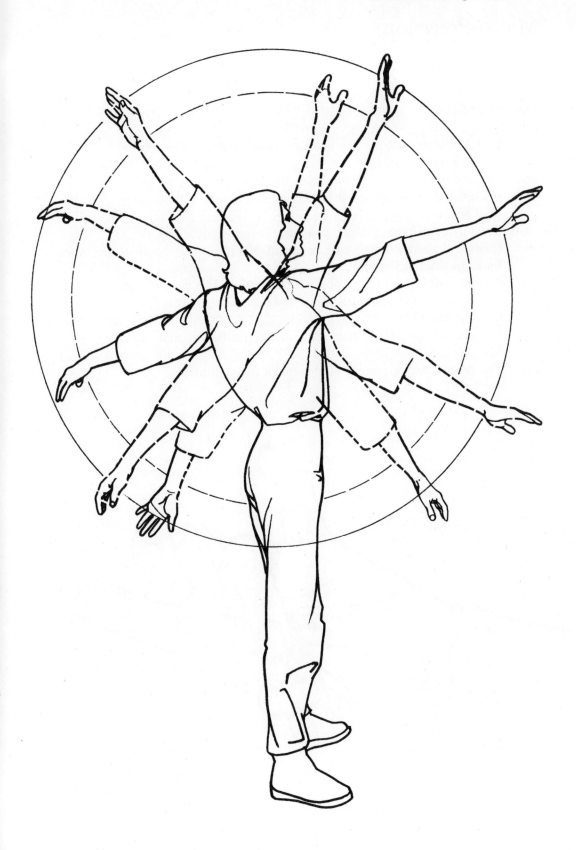

Micro-Precision

Micro-precision 1

Roll 2 little sticky balls (for instance, chewing gum) between the fingers of both hands

a–d. Thumb–index finger (nail phalanx), thumb–middle finger (nail phalanx), thumb–ring finger (nail phalanx), thumb–little finger (nail phalanx)

e–h. Thumb–index finger (middle phalanx), thumb–middle finger (middle phalanx), thumb–ring finger (middle phalanx), thumb–little finger (middle phalanx)

i–l. Thumb–index finger (palm phalanx), thumb–middle finger (palm phalanx), thumb–ring finger (palm phalanx), thumb–little finger (palm phalanx)

Movement: linear (both horizontal and vertical), diagonal, circular, figure 8

Tip: try a different pattern of movement for each hand

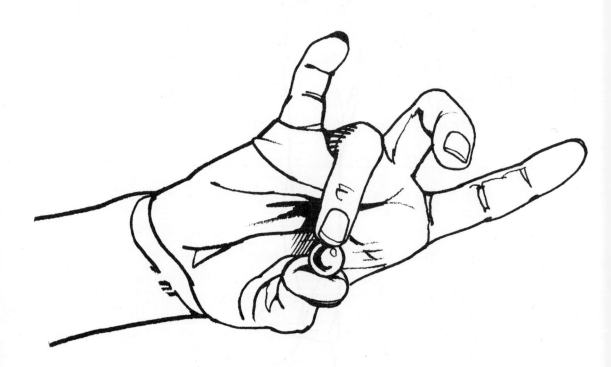

Micro-precision 2

First, draw a, then b (with the right hand)
Draw a (with the right hand) and b (with the left hand) simultaneously
Important: keep the drawing relatively small (approximptely 1½″–2″)

Micro-precision 3

Draw the above figure and continue to follow its lines
a. With the right hand only
b. With both the right hand and the left hand (2 figures simultaneously)
Important: keep the drawings relatively small (approximately 1″)

NOTES:
Try to feel your way toward a hand position which allows you to draw and/or write more comfortably.

Hand-eye co-ordination
a.a. Starting position: right eye open, left eye shut
Focus upon an object
Reach out your right hand, bring the tip of the little finger in line with the direction you are looking in, let the little finger "scan" the object (draw its outlines in the air)
The kinetic force is generated in the palm joint
a.b. The kinetic force is generated in the wrist
a.c. The kinetic force is generated in the elbow
a.d. The kinetic force is generated in the shoulder
b. Right eye open, left hand draws
c. Left eye open, right hand draws
d. Left eye open, left hand draws

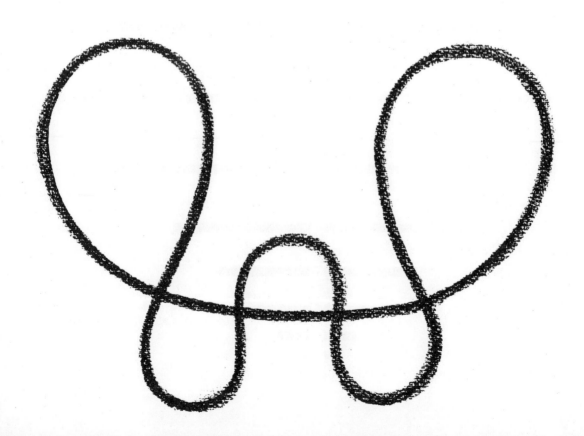

Co-Ordination

Co-ordination 1

a. Rotate an unbreakable object (disc, ball, etc.) around the body
   (transfer it from one hand to the other; once in front, once behind;
   repeat continuously)
   Tempo: moderately fast (above all, regular)
   Duration: first ± 30 sec clockwise, then ± 30 sec counter-clockwise

b. The object is thrown from one hand to the other (apart from that, the
   same as in a.).
   Tip: try the same in group formation, for example, 3 people stand in
   a circle and simultaneously hand each other their objects (both clockwise and counter-clockwise; both in front of and behind the body)

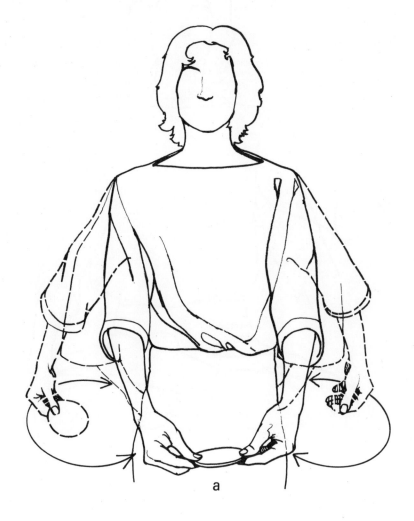

a

Co-ordination 2

Rhythmic "drumming"

a. With arms stretched (the kinetic force is generated in the shoulders and upper arms only)

b. With the lower arms (not too forceful, upper arms remain immobile)

a

b

   c.   With the hands (upper and lower arms remain immobile)

   d.   With fingers (all at once)

e–i. First with the thumbs, then with the index fingers, middle fingers, ring fingers and little fingers

Rhythm: R: once, L: once, R: twice, L: twice, R: 3 times, L: 3 times, R: twice, L: twice

Repeat continuously

Tempo: comfortable (above all, regular)

Duration: ±30 sec per unit of exercise

Tip: try the same with musical accompaniment and/or other rhythmic patterns

c

Co-ordination 3

a. Clap palm against palm
b. Clap right fist against palm
c. Clap palm against palm again
d. Clap left fist against palm
    Again, a–d, repeat continuously
    Rhythm: regular
    Tempo: depending on level of advancement
e–h. Variations: instead of fist on palm, palm on back of the hand combined
    with a+c palm against palm
    Try this in the following order: a–d, e–h, a–d, e–h, etc.

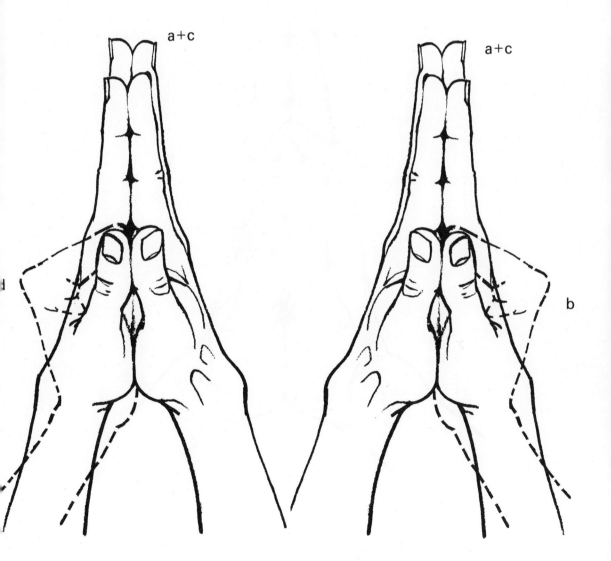

Co-ordination 4

Fingers swing around each other (repeat continuously)
Units of exercise: 1, 2, 3, 4, 5, then 1+2, 2+3, 3+4, 4+5, then
1+2+3, 2+3+4, 3+4+5, then 1+2+3+4, 1+2+3+5, 1+2+4+5,
1+3+4+5, 2+3+4+5, then 1+2+3+4+5

2

Tempo: comfortable (above all, regular)

Duration: ±10 sec per unit of exercise

Variations: try combinations like 2+4:

1. In the above-mentioned way: both fingers of the right hand move upwards, while both fingers of the left hand move downwards and vice versa.

2. In an alternative way: both fingers of the right hand move inwards, while both fingers of the left hand move outwards and vice versa.

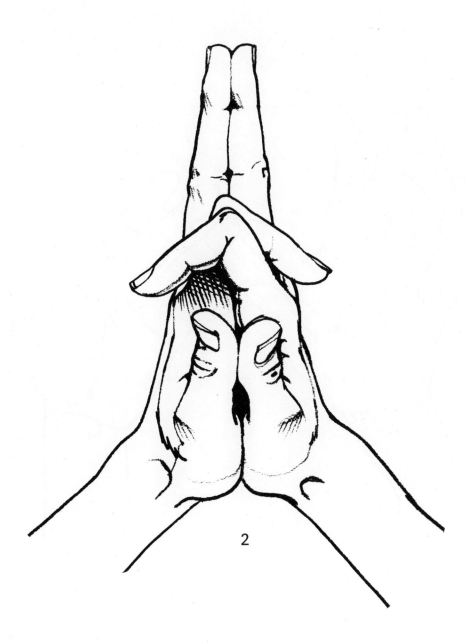

2

Co-ordination 5

   a.   Tip of left thumb touching nail phalanx of right little finger
   b.   Tip of right thumb touching nail phalanx of left little finger
   c.   Left thumb touching nail phalanx of right ring finger
   d.   Right thumb touching nail phalanx of left ring finger
   e.   Left thumb touching nail phalanx of right middle finger
   f.   Right thumb touching nail phalanx of left middle finger
   g.   Left thumb touching nail phalanx of right index finger

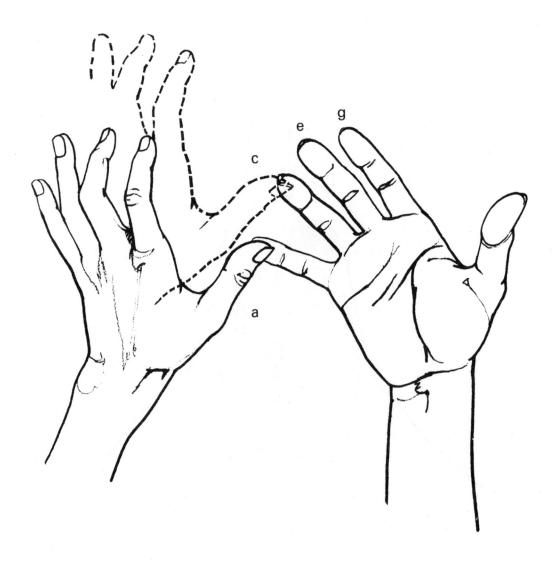

h. Right thumb touching nail phalanx of left index finger
    Again, a–h, repeat continuously (variation: a–b–c–d–e–f–g–h–e–f–c–d,
    repeat continuously)
i–p. Tip of thumb touching middle phalanx
q–z. Tip of thumb touching palm phalanx
    Tempo: depending on level of advancement (above all, regular)
    Duration: a–h 30 sec, i–p 30 sec, q–z 30 sec (or longer)

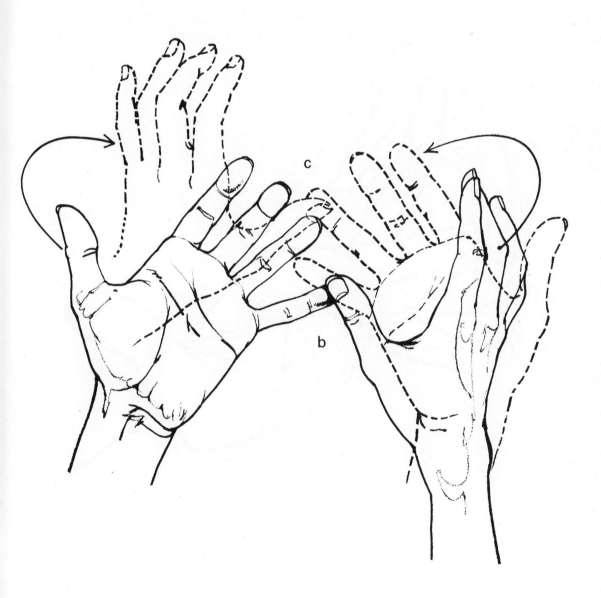

Co-ordination 6

   a.   Index and little fingers turn around middle and ring fingers (repeat
       continuously)
   b.   Index and ring fingers turn around middle fingers (repeat continuously)
   c.   Middle and little fingers turn around ring fingers (repeat continuously)
       Tempo: comfortable (above all, regular)
       Duration: ±15 sec per unit of exercise

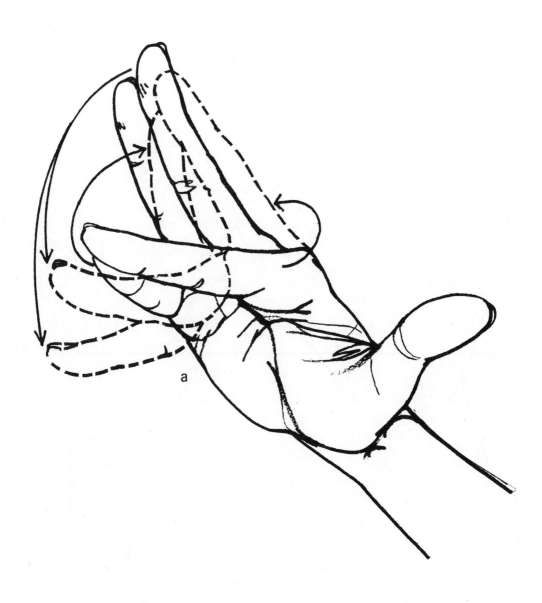

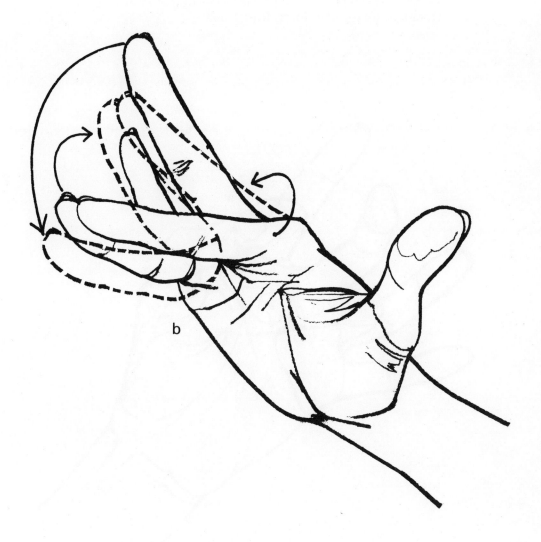

b

Co-ordination 7

With both hands simultaneously:
a. Tip of thumb on tip of index finger
b. Tip of thumb on tip of ring finger
c. Tip of thumb on tip of middle finger
d. Tip of thumb on tip of little finger
Again, a–d . . . repeat continuously
Variations: d–a–c–b or a–c–d–b or L: a–d, then R: d–a, etc.
Tempo: depending on level of advancement (above all, regular)
Duration: all together for at least 1 min

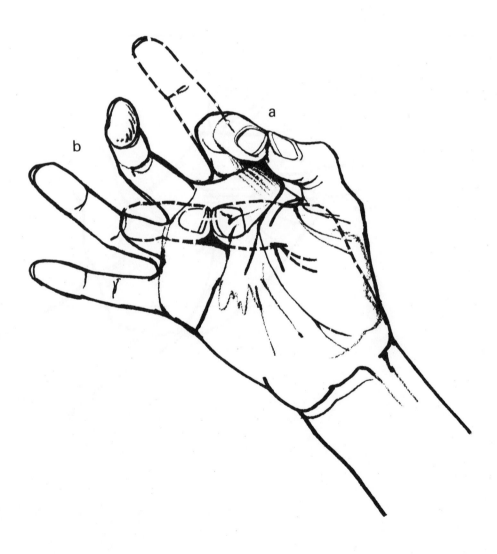

Co-ordination 8

Bending/stretching with both hands (fingers from middle joints, thumbs from nail joints, ±10 times)

a. 1, 2, 3, 4, 5,
b. 1+2, 2+3, 3+4, 4+5
c. 1+3, 2+4, 3+5
d. 1+4, 2+5
e. 1+5
f. 1+2+3 (twice), 1+3+4+(twice), 1+2+3 (twice) 1+4+5 (twice), repeat 5 times
g. 1+2+5 (twice), 1+2+4 (twice), 1+2+5 (twice), 1+3+5 (twice), repeat 5 times
h. 2+3+4 (once), 2+4+5 (once), 2+3+5 (once), 3+4+5 (once), repeat 5 times
i. 2+3+4+5, 1+3+4+5, 1+2+4+5, 1+2+3+5, 1+2+3+4
j. 1+2+3+4+5
k–q The same with fingers stretched (the kinetic force is generated in the palm joints only)
Variations: L:1, R:5, then L:2, R:4, then L:3, R:3, then L:4, R:2, then L:5, R:1, repeat continuously. At a more advanced stage, one might try other, more difficult left-right combinations as well
Tempo: comfortable (above all, regular)
Duration: depending on level of advancement

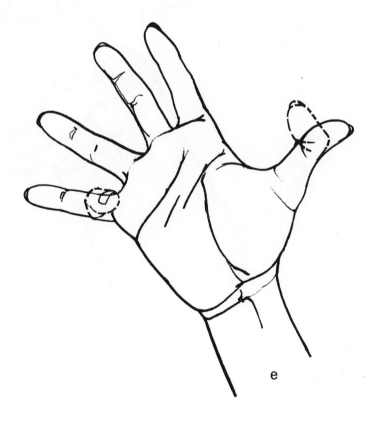

e

Co-ordination 9

Rotation of the thumb
a. Right thumb forward, left thumb backward (repeat continuously, simultaneously)
b. The same in opposite directions
Tempo: comfortable
Duration: ±20 sec per unit of exercise
Tip: if you find it difficult to perform the exercise as described, try once rotation left, stop, then once rotation right, stop, then once rotation left, stop, then once rotation right, stop, etc.

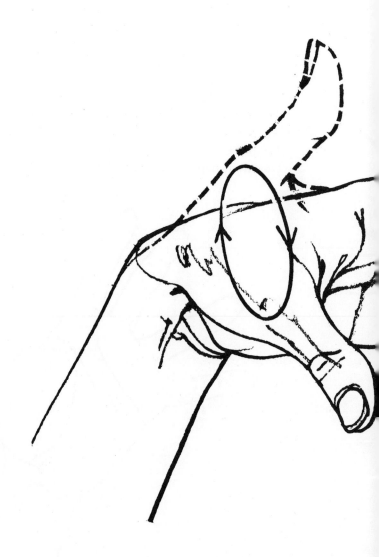

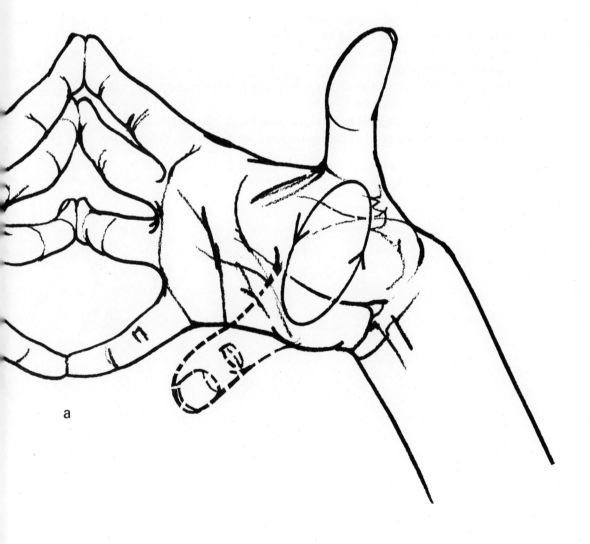

a

Co-ordination 10

a. Both hands rotate clockwise at equal speed (comfortable tempo)
b. Right hand maintains its speed, left hand gradually slows down its speed of rotation
c. Right hand maintains its speed, left hand comes to a standstill
d. Right hand maintains its speed, left hand accelerates counter-clockwise
e. Both hands rotate at equal speed (right hand clockwise, left hand counter-clockwise)
f–h. Left hand maintains its speed, right hand gradually slows down, stops, then accelerates counter-clockwise
i. Both hands rotate counter-clockwise at equal speed
j–l. Right hand maintains its speed, left hand gradually slows down, stops, then accelerates clockwise
m. Both hands rotate at equal speed (right hand counter-clockwise, left hand clockwise)
n–p. Left hand maintains its speed, right hand gradually slows down, stops, then accelerates clockwise (until a)
Repeat a–p several times
Duration: unlimited
Important: this exercise is ideal for learning how to master the basic principles of co-ordination
Tip: if you find it difficult to "unlink" the hands' directions and/or speeds, try rotating one hand continuously while the other moves "jerk by jerk"

b

Co-ordination 11

Rotation of the shoulders
a. Left shoulder forward, right shoulder backward (repeat continuously, simultaneously)
b. The same in opposite directions
Tempo: comfortable
Duration: ±15 sec per unit of exercise
Tip: if you find it difficult to perform the exercise as described, try once rotation left, stop, then once rotation right, stop, then once rotation left, stop, then once rotation right, stop, etc.

a

Co-ordination 12

    a.   Arms rotate at equal speed (comfortable tempo)
    b.   Left arm gradually slows down its speed of rotation

c.   After stopping, left arm accelerates in opposite direction

d.   The same with the right arm (as soon as both arms rotate at equal speed)

Duration: altogether ±2 min

e.   Arms move in a cubical pattern (parallel)

f.   The same pattern of movement, "non-parallel" (arms in a 90° position)

g.   Arms in a 180° position

Tempo: comfortable

Duration: ±1 min

Tip: to bridge initial difficulties, "draw" the cubical pattern first of all within visual range in front of the body, then let it gradually grow in size toward the sides (to visualize this figure, imagine standing between 2 blackboards with a piece of chalk in each hand)

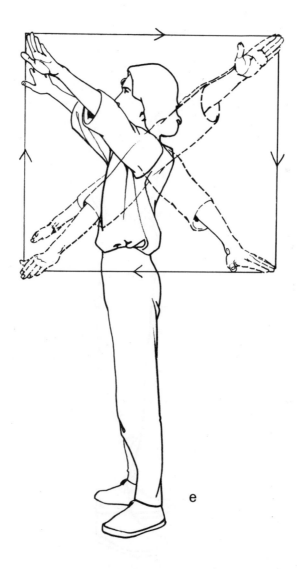

e

h. Arms move in a triangular pattern (1 triangle pointing up, 1 triangle pointing down; parallel)
i. The same pattern of movement "non-parallel" (arms in a 90° position)
j. Arms in a 180° position
    Tempo: comfortable
    Duration: ±1 min
    Tip: in a more advanced stage, circle, cube and triangle can be combined with each other

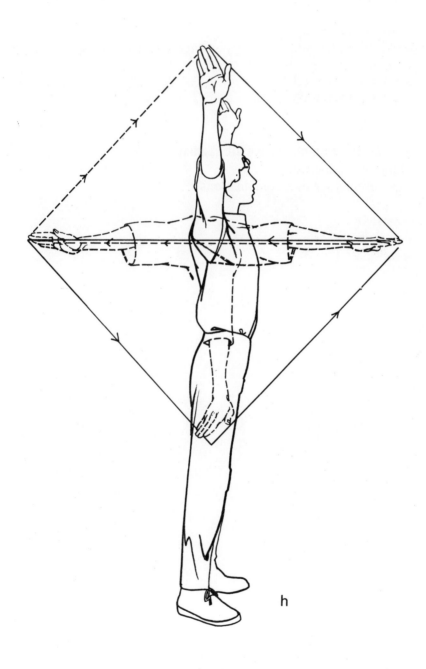

h

NOTES:

Explanation of numerical code:

1=thumb, 2=index finger, 3=middle finger, 4=ring-finger, 5=little finger

Try the following:

Accompany an appropriate piece of music with rhythmic clapping.

Alternate between "left-hand-below/right-hand-above" and "right-hand-below/left-hand-above."

You will find this simple exercise to be a surprisingly effective catalyst for developing a sense of rhythm.

Equally worthwhile trying:

Put both hands on the table. Move your fingers as if you were playing piano.

   Pattern of movement:

a.   4 5 3 4 5 3 4 3 5 4 3 5

b.   3 4 2 3 4 2 3 2 4 3 2 4

c.   2 3 1 2 3 1 2 1 3 2 1 3

   Then b, then a

   Tempo: comfortable (above all, regular)

   Duration: unlimited

   Tip: invent your own combinations

Related exercises:

Condition training—arms (see NOTES)

Micro-precision 1+2+3

Flexibility 1

Esthetics 1

Flexibility

Flexibility 1

Starting position: put the little fingers in two imaginary keyholes
a. Arms and hands turn around the axis (arms stretched forwards, elbows slightly bent; repeat continuously)
b. The same with arms stretched sideways
c. The same with arms stretched upwards
d. Transfer axis to ring fingers (arms stretched forwards)
e. Sideways
f. Upwards
g. Transfer axis to middle fingers (forwards)
h. Sideways
i. Upwards
j. Transfer axis to index fingers (forwards)
k. Sideways
l. Upwards
m. Transfer axis to thumbs (both arms and thumbs stretched forwards)
n. Sideways
o. Upwards
  Tempo: moderately fast
  Duration: ± 10 sec per unit of exercise

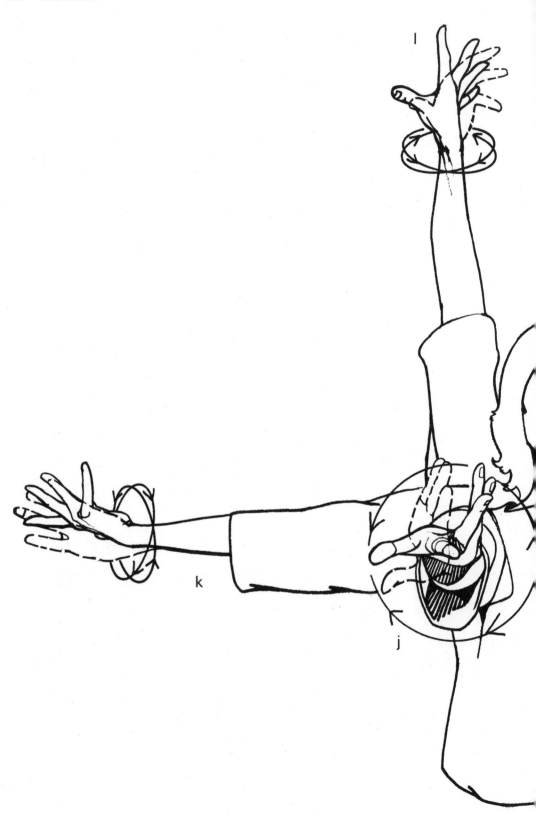

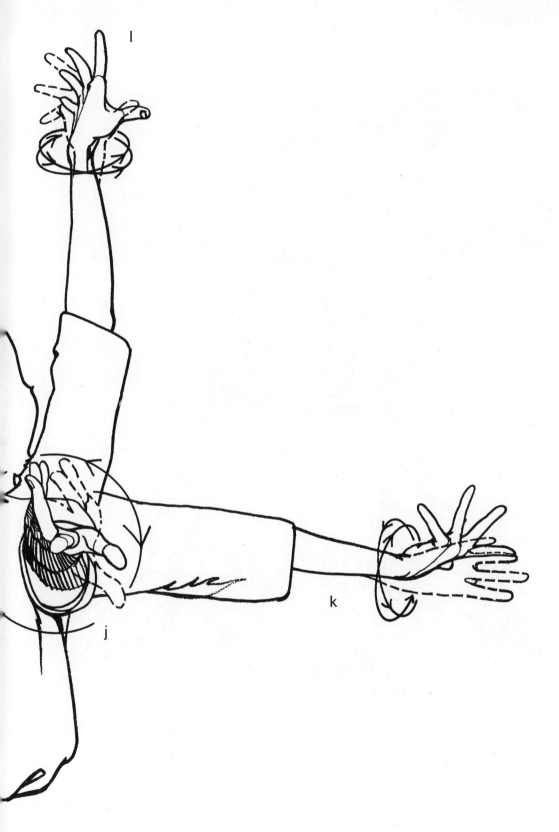

Flexibility 2

a. Hands "swishing" upwards
b. Hands dropping while turning 180° around their axis
c. Hands "swishing" downwards
d. Hands "swishing" upwards while turning 180°
    Repeat a–d continuously
    Tempo: once a–d per sec (or slightly faster)
    Duration: ±30 sec
    Important: dynamic relaxation of both hands is an essential prerequisite
    for this exercise (the kinetic force is generated in the lower arms only)

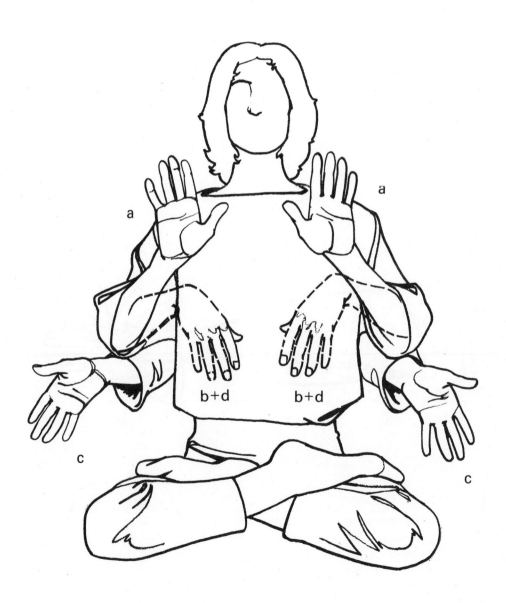

Flexibility 3

a. Left middle finger on tip of right little finger
    The fingers, which are not fixed, co-ordinate into an undulating
    motion (first 10 times to the right, then 10 times to the left)
b. Left middle finger on tip of right ring-finger
c. Left middle finger on tip of right middle finger
d. Left middle finger on tip of right index finger
e. Tip of left middle finger on the same spot as where the thumb was,
    tip of left thumb on tip of right thumb; resume undulating motion
f–j. The same with the left hand
    Tempo: comfortable

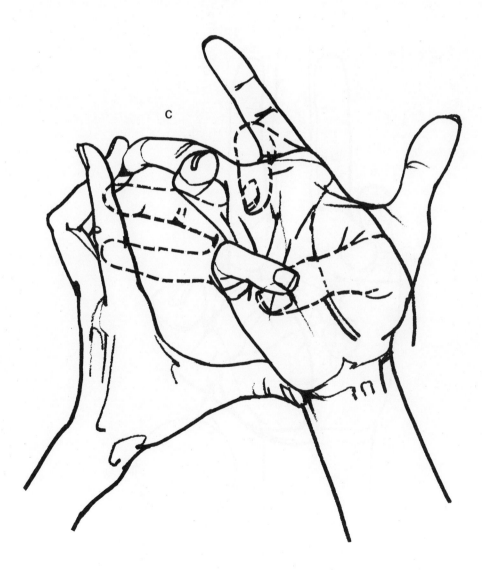

Flexibility 4

With both hands simultaneously
a.   Rotate folded thumb in both directions
b.   The same with index fingers, bent
c.   The same with middle fingers, bent
d.   The same with ring-fingers, bent
e.   The same with little fingers, bent
Tempo: comfortable
Duration: ±5 sec per direction of rotation
Important: b–e are to be practiced in an advanced stage only.
If you restrict yourself to a, the duration of exercise should be
slightly longer

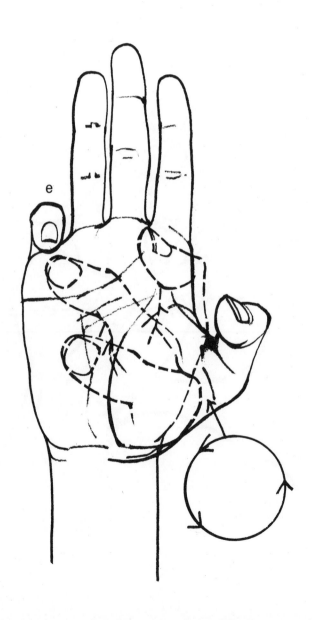

Flexibility 5

a. Pen between the tip of the thumb and the little finger, move wrist in a figure 8 pattern (if possible with 2 pens, that is to say, using both hands)

b–d. Thumb–ring-finger, thumb–middle finger, thumb–index finger
Tempo: comfortable
Duration: ± 30 sec per unit of exercise
Variation: by using shorter sticks (1, 2, 3 or 4 for each hand) you may invent your own combinations

Related exercises:
Condition training—hands (in its entirety)
Condition training—arms (see NOTES)
Sensitivity $1+2+3+4+5$
Psychophysical balance $1+2+3$
Hand-brain feedback 2

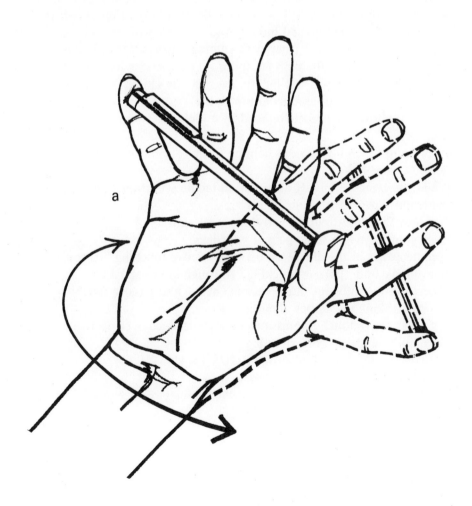

Sensitivity

Sensitivity 1

   a.   Starting position: choose a spot on the floor where a great variety of textures are within easy reach
Close your eyes

a.a.   Let your hands explore the "feel" of things (± 3 min)

a.b.   Slow down your movements (this will add more concentration to what you perceive)
Touch the carpet with your palms only (± 30 sec), with your fingers (± 30 sec), with the back of your hands (± 30 sec), with the back of your fingers (± 30 sec), with each separate fingertip (± 15 sec per finger)

a.c.   Perceive the difference between touching an object with one hand ("mono") and two hands ("stereo"), with awareness focused on form (instead of "thingness"), with awareness focused on texture (instead of form or "thingness"), with awareness focused in the thumb (where we usually have accumulated most of our energy), with awareness focused in the little finger (therewith gaining a new sense of balance which, in turn, clears the path for more subtle energies to flow in)

   b.   Starting position: hands rest on lap, eyes remain closed

b.a.   Become aware of your skin from top to toe
Experience how you are surrounded by a global network of touch receptors
Open up to touch impressions coming from your buttocks, your clothing, your hair . . .

b.b.   While you remain globally aware of all tactile sensations, start making gentle movements with your hands
Feel how the air currents are stroking your skin

b.c.   Place your palms on some part of your legs
Become aware of the difference between "active touching" (through your hands) and "passive touching" (through your legs)
Experience the different ratios between active and passive touching by first stroking the carpet, then the legs
Try to let active touch impressions take precedence over passive ones

b.d.   Place both hands on your right leg
Use your sense of touch to probe BELOW the skin
Explore other parts of the body as well
Be especially alert to whether or not the muscles you feel are in a state of tension

If so, try to relax them by means of massage (it may help to visualize the body as a child which is being cared for by the sensitive hands of a loving mother)

Bring both hands to your neck-shoulder area (where tension builds up most easily)

Allow your head to drop backwards (after you start massaging again)

b.e.   Place all ten fingertips on your forehead

At the slowest possible speed, lower your fingertips all the way down to your neck (do not apply pressure, allow your fingertips to adjust flexibly to the natural shape of what they are sensing)

Applying the same "soft sensing technique," use only one finger of each hand to explore your profile with utmost attention

Do the same with other parts of the body

Sensitivity 2

Exploring the dimensions of touch (with little finger)
a. Back of the hand
b. Palm
c. Lower arm
d. Upper arm
Tempo: slow

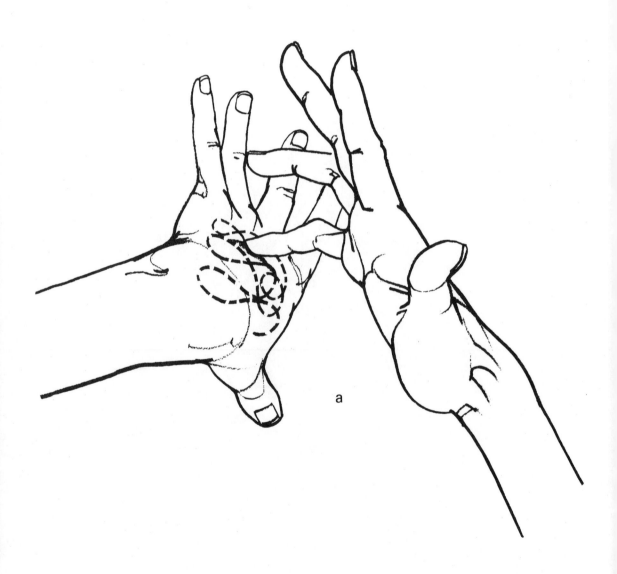

a

Sensitivity 3

"Palm-on-palm" rotation
a.   Around the palm joints

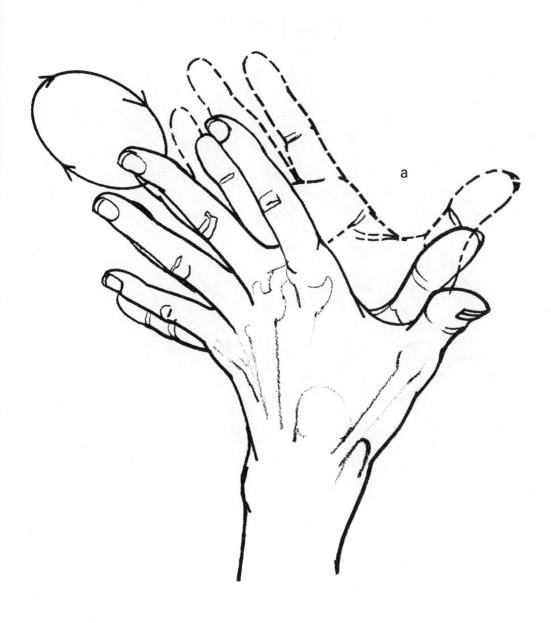

b. Around the heels
    Tempo: comfortable

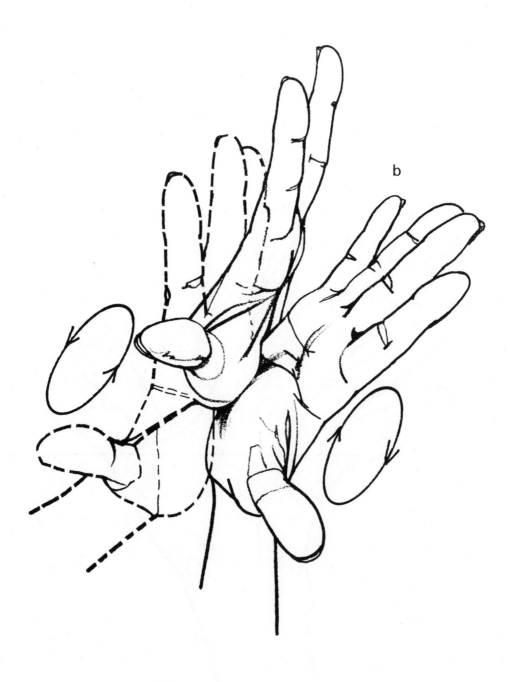

Sensitivity 4

Minimal touch
a. Palms facing each other

a

    b. Fingertips only

    c. Stroking of lower and upper arms (in slow tempo)

    d. The same with other parts of the body

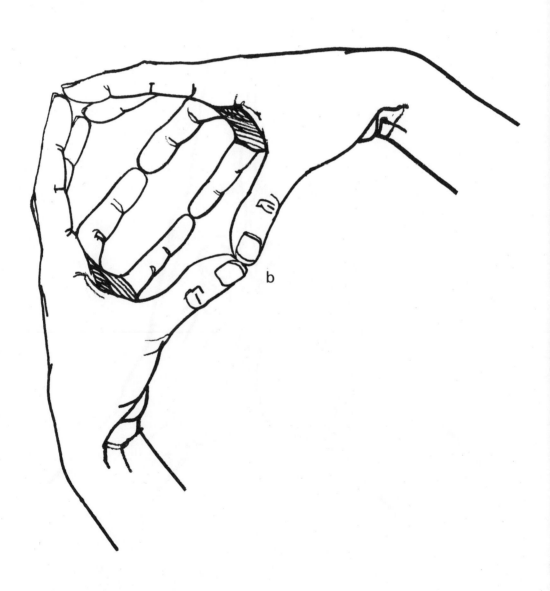

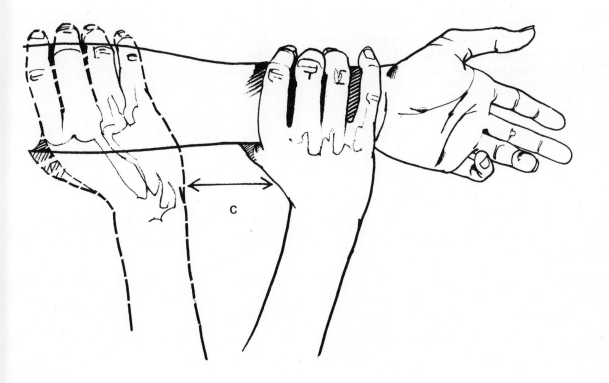

Sensitivity 5

Expressing tenderness
a. By caressing oneself
b. By caressing children and/or pets
c. By caressing friends (avoid sexual connotations; let them know about the development process you are going through)

NOTES:
To be able to gain the full bounty of physical contact one must first engender an inner receptivity (that is to say, a space must be created in which the increasingly more subtle shades of perception can band together spectrally).

Any attempt in this direction requires a real effort to explore the tactile qualities of everything we have grown "out of touch" with.

Those who regularly re-sensitize themselves in this way will see their awareness of reality infinitely enriched.

Related exercises:
Condition training—arms (see NOTES)
Psychophysical balance 3
Hand-brain feedback 2
Bio-energy 1+2

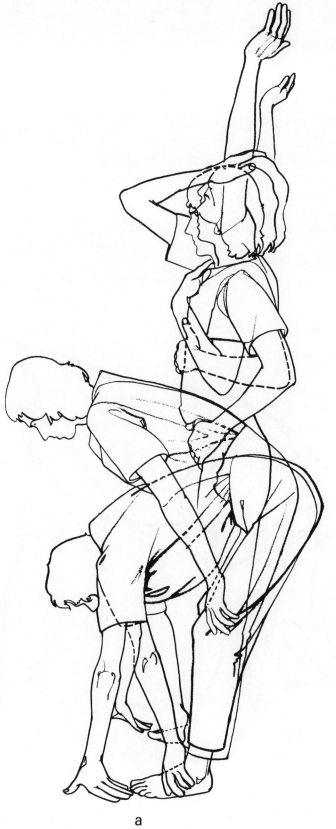

a

Dynamic Relaxation

Dynamic relaxation 1

Starting position: upper arms horizontal, hands relaxed
Hand "swishing" forwards and backwards (the kinetic force is
generated in the lower arms only)
Tempo: fast
Duration: 15 sec (or longer)

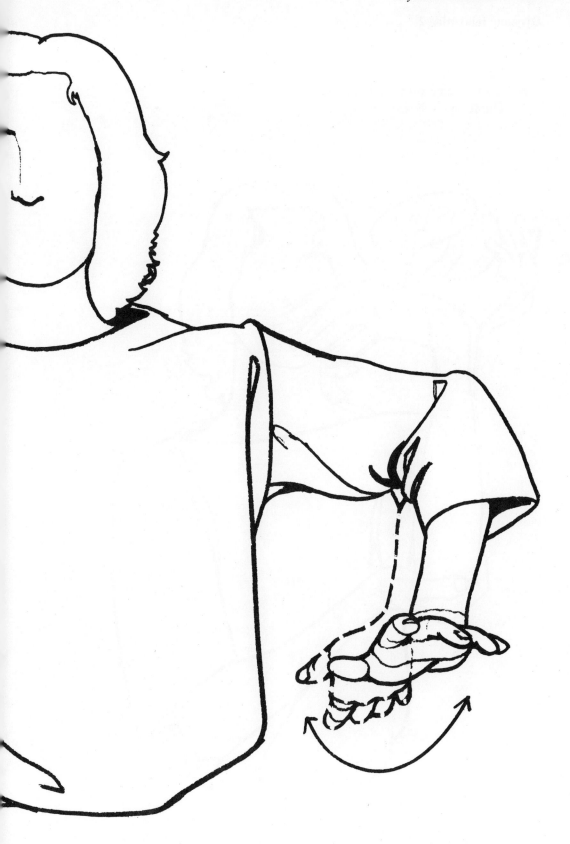

Dynamic relaxation 2

a. Support the right lower arm with the left hand, let the (relaxed) right hand "whirl"
b. Do the same with the left hand
   Duration: ±30 sec

a

c. Grab the right upper arm with the left hand (near the shoulder, press the upper arm against the chest)
   Let the (relaxed) lower arm and hand "whirl"
d. Do the same with the right-hand/lower-arm

c

Dynamic relaxation 3

a. Left thumb on the most sensitive "press button" of right hand, let left hand "swish" right hand
b. Do the same with the other hand

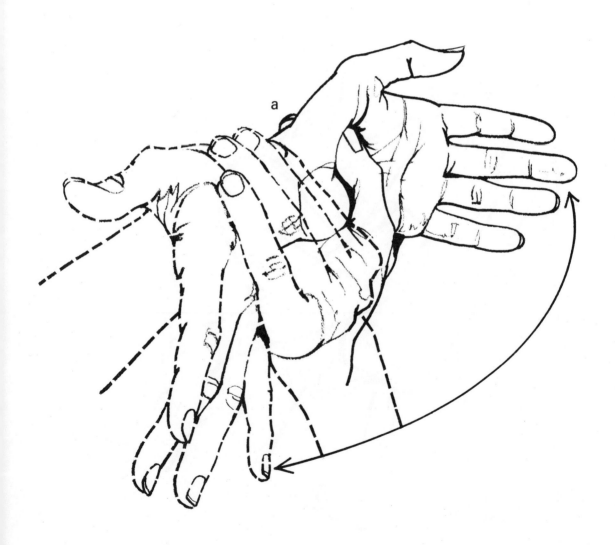

c. Left thumb on "press button" (near the wrist) of right hand, let left hand "swish" right hand

d. Do the same with the other hand

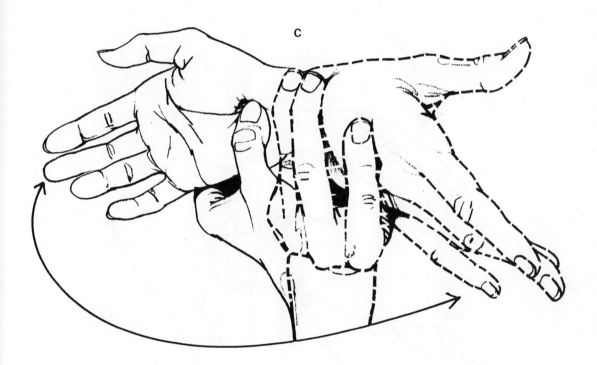

c

e. Left thumb on "press button" (just under the wrist bone) of the right hand, let left hand "swish" right hand

f. Do the same with the other hand

Tempo: fast

Duration: ±15 sec per unit of exercise

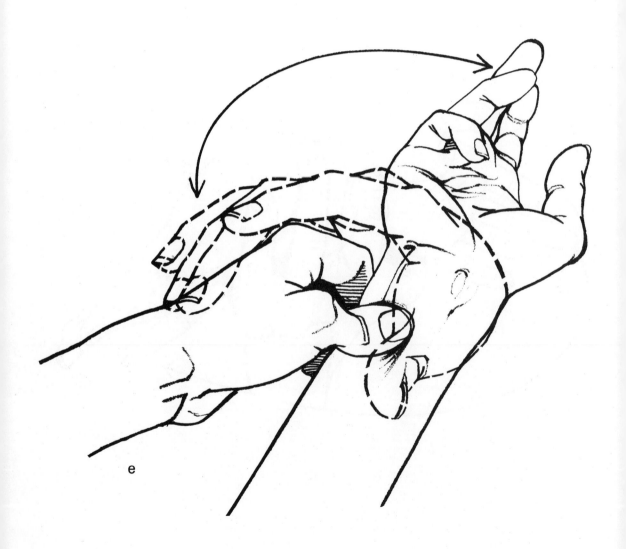

e

g. While the right hand is rotating clockwise, let the left thumb press on indicated points (point by point)

h. While the right hand is rotating counter-clockwise, let the left thumb press on indicated points

i+j. Do the same with the other arm

Rhythm: 1 rotation per point

Tempo: moderately fast

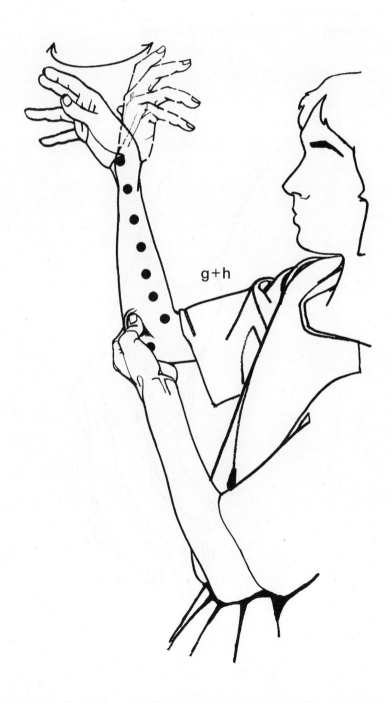

g+h

Dynamic relaxation 4

Starting position: arms hanging alongside the body; evoke a muscular vibration in:

a. The thumbs
b. The index fingers
c. The middle fingers
d. The ring fingers
e. The little fingers
f. The whole hand
    Duration: $\pm$ 10 sec per unit of exercise

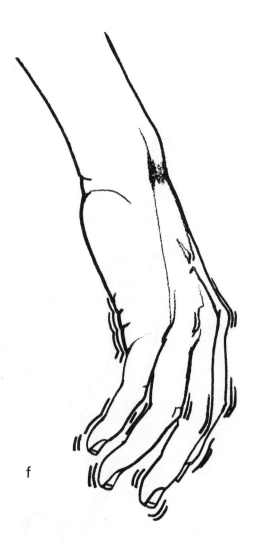

f

Dynamic relaxation 5

a.   Mobilize the palm phalanx (gently)
b.   Then the middle phalanx
c.   Then the nail phalanx
    Tempo: slow
    Duration: ±15 sec per finger
    Tip: you may prefer the following finger position: the thumb below,
    the index and middle finger on top of the phalanx

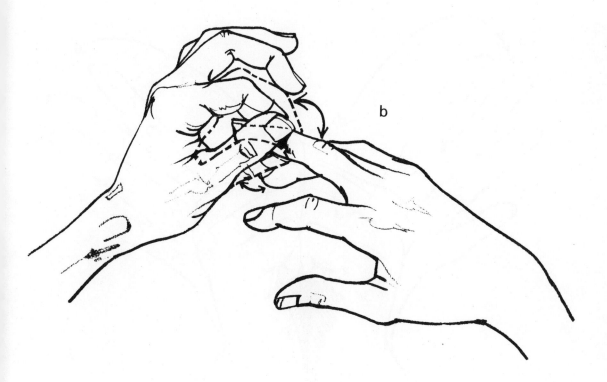

Dynamic relaxation 6

Starting position: hands about 6″–8″ in front of the head
Keep the rest of the body relaxed and breathe through the nose

a–b. Inhale (take in the "Light"): the "lotus" is slowly opening itself

b–a. Exhale (expel all "Darkness"): the "lotus" is slowly closing itself
Tempo: continuously decreasing (without effort)
Duration: to be determined by intuition only

  c. As you continue opening/closing, the hands slowly move apart
Let them come to rest on your knees
Important: let the "lotus" motion respond to (not interfere with) the
natural pulsing rhythm of your breathing

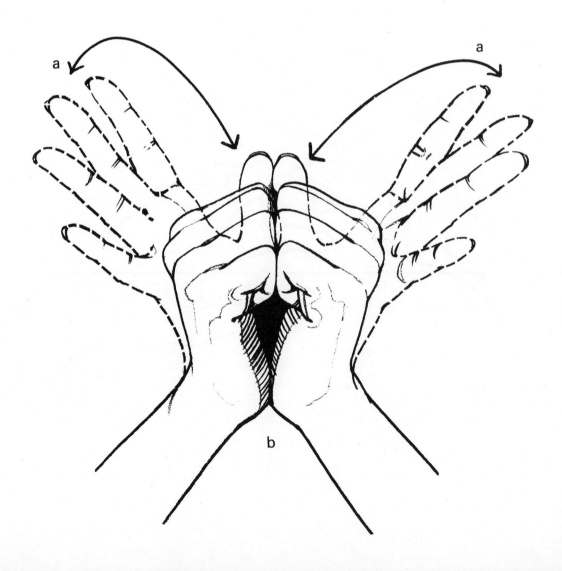

NOTES:

The neuro-muscular dynamism of the body is based on the interplay of three different kinds of tension:

REMNANT TENSION=activity level of relaxed muscles ("tonus")
MOBILIZING TENSION=dynamic muscle activity
STABILIZING TENSION=fix muscle activity

Mobilizing tension causes strength, speed and flexibility.
Stabilizing tension gives movements their pattern and precision.
   Normal functioning requires a well-proportioned combination of both.
For the sake of stress-prevention, however, three basic rules should always be observed:

1. Don't ever generate more tension than necessary
2. Let go of all tension as soon as its actual task is completed (eliminate useless activity . . . keep your energy in a state of quiescence so that when action is required, it can be summoned and applied with the highest possible degree of ease and efficiency)
3. Let "natural flow" be the key-tone to which all your movements resonate.

Try "Flexibility 1" with arms hanging down. Even though in this position the exercise may have less of a strengthening effect upon the muscles; it is, especially because of that, very well-suited for swiftly getting the entire hand-arm system into a state of suppleness.
"Condition training—arms 6" is an ideal exercise for eliminating tensions in the neck and/or the shoulders.

Related exercises:
Condition training—hands 1+7
Condition training—arms 5+6
Passive relaxation 1+2+3
Psychophysical balance 2+3
Hand-brain feedback 3
Bio-energy 1+2+3e

Passive Relaxation

Passive relaxation 1

Hands in resting position:
Arms hanging alongside the body, hand and arm muscles completely relaxed
Important: feel the release of pent-up energy
Tip: take a meditative walk with both hands in resting position

Passive relaxation 2

a. Let one arm become "heavy"
b. Do the same with the other arm
c. Lean forward (without support), let both arms become "heavy"
   Duration: $\pm$45 sec per unit of exercise

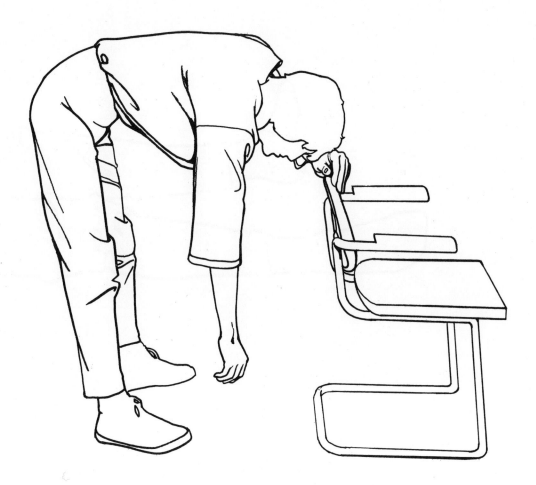

Passive relaxation 3

Total relaxation

NOTES:
Try to feel your heart-beat in the entire body (especially in the hands).

Related exercises:
Hand-brain feedback 1

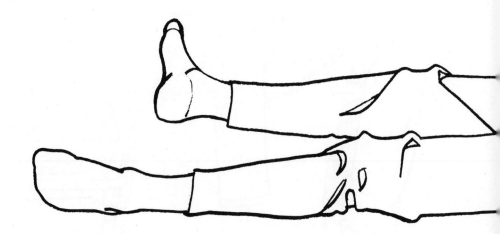

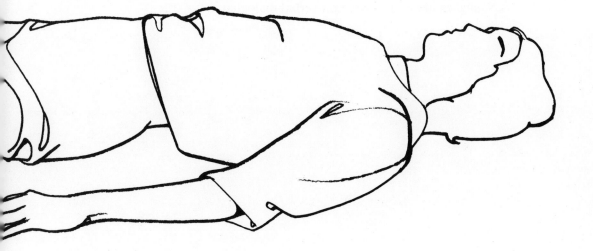

Expression

Expression 1

Non-verbal communication
- a.   Expression of feelings
- a.a.   Exchange non-verbal signals of friendship
- a.b.   Then signals of affirmation and solidarity
- a.c.   Then signals of love and affection
- b.   Pantomime
- b.a.   Represent an existing object by non-verbal means only, and let your partner guess what it is (change roles, $\pm$ 5 times)
- b.b.   Subsequently, an idea and/or feeling ($\pm$5 times)
- b.c.   Subsequently, a short story ($\pm$3 times)
  Tip: instead of guessing each others' ideas, feelings and/or short stories it may be easier to let one partner suggest what the other is to express
- b.d.   Communicate non-verbally the most dramatic events of your life, from the time of conception to the present, with eyes closed
- c.   Echoing of behavior
- c.a.   One partner sets the pattern of movement, then the other tries to imitate it simultaneously (change roles)
- c.b.   Establish a mutual response and harmonize on all levels (that is to say, engage in an intuitive, non-verbal dialogue)

a

Expression 2

a. Inventory of one's repertoire of non-verbal expressions

a.a. Trace all gestures and/or mannerisms which are part of your everyday life

a.b. Become aware of the various "body dialects" existing in society

a.c. Which style of communication do you share with whom?

b. Explore alternative possibilities of expression

b.a. Study pictures and/or paintings of various people and imitate their poses (this will enable you to actually experience someone's expressive intent)

b.b. Assimilation of behavior: study the behavioral patterns of people, who make an extraordinarily positive impression on you and assimilate that part of their expressiveness which resonates with your own inner being (through this method you may actualize previously undiscovered growth potentials)

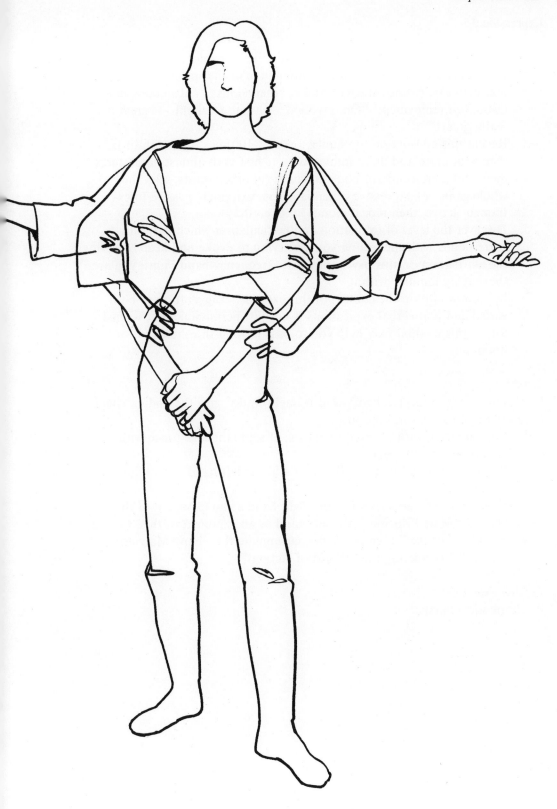

Expression 3

a. Select a specific feeling which you would like to explore and/or intensify
b. Formulate a concise affirmation connotative of that particular feeling: that is to say, (wonderment) "Ahh . . . marvelous . . . absolutely fantastic!" or (enjoyment) "Oh, my God . . . what a delight . . . great . . . really great!"
c. Repeat this affirmation (or similar ones) ±10 times, first with little, then with more and more intonation, . . . first with almost no gestures, then with a crescendo of body language (in other words, scan the whole gamut of expressive potentials from extremely passive to extremely active, then repeat c once in its entirety)
d. Discover the level of intonation and gesticulation which naturally corresponds with the feeling you are trying to evoke and keep repeating the affirmation on this psychophysical "frequency band" until you are thoroughly familiar with it
    Important: within the context of this exercise, exaggeration of both verbal and non-verbal expressions is not just permissible, but wished for, as this method may help you to pass beyond thresholds of inhibition

NOTES:
Don't always try to tell the body what it ought to do; give the body a chance to reveal to you its natural purpose:
a. Communicate with yourself by means of sign language (once with, once without a mirror)
b. Perform a manual play (let the right and the left hand "speak" to each other)
c. Close your eyes and visualize the right hand as an exponent of the "Cosmic Male Principle," the left hand as an exponent of the "Cosmic Female Principle," then let them consummate the "Holy Marriage," therewith co-creating the "World of Action"

Related exercises:
Psychophysical balance 3

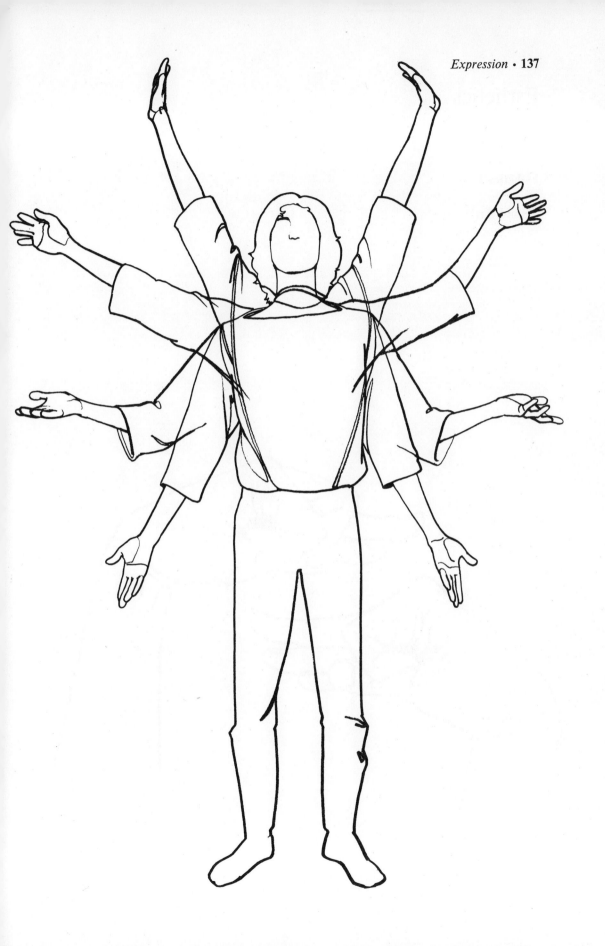

Esthetics

Esthetics 1

"Hand Art"

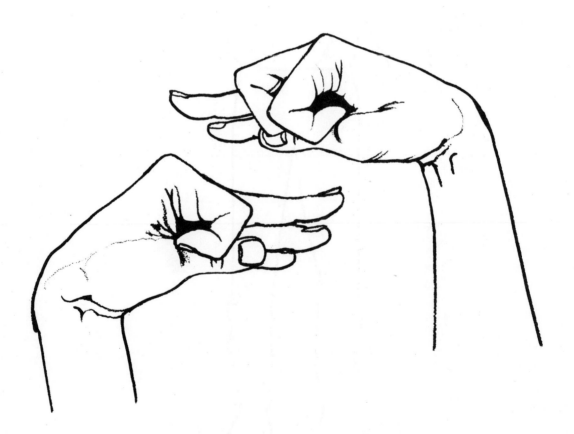

Esthetics 2

Lotus Cycle: a–b–c–d–e–f–g–h–g–f–e–d–c–b–a

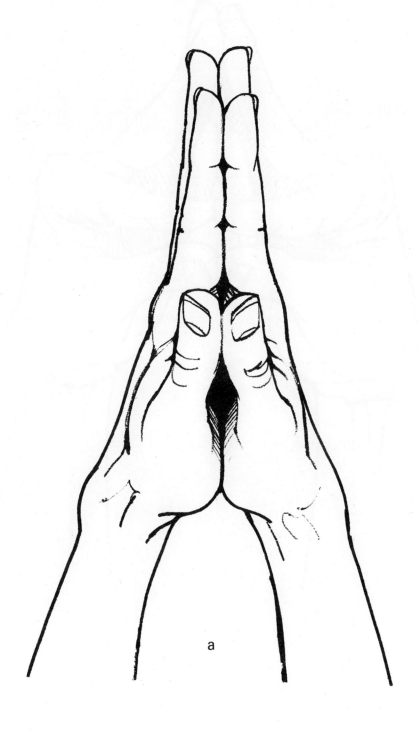

a

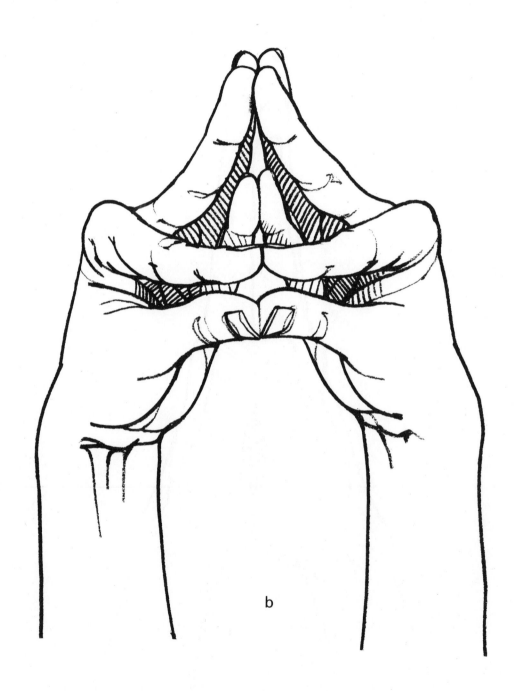

b

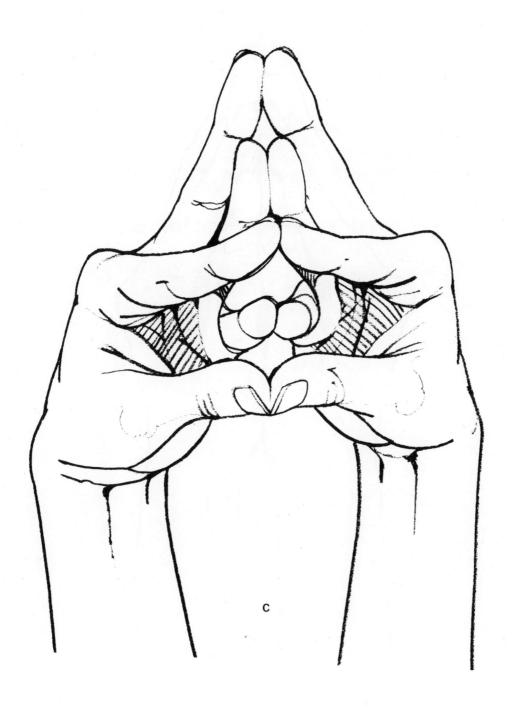

c

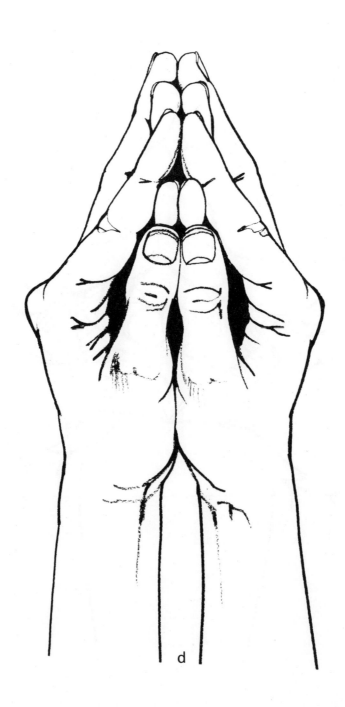

d

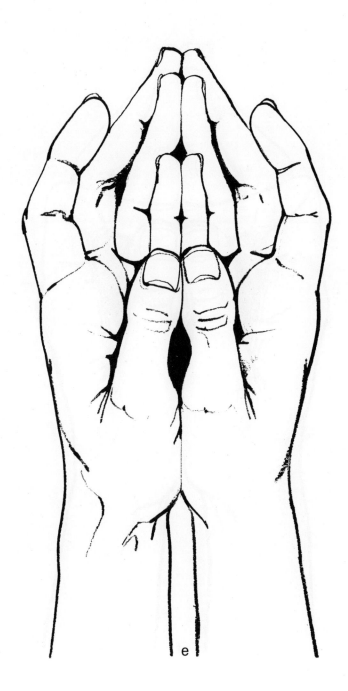

e

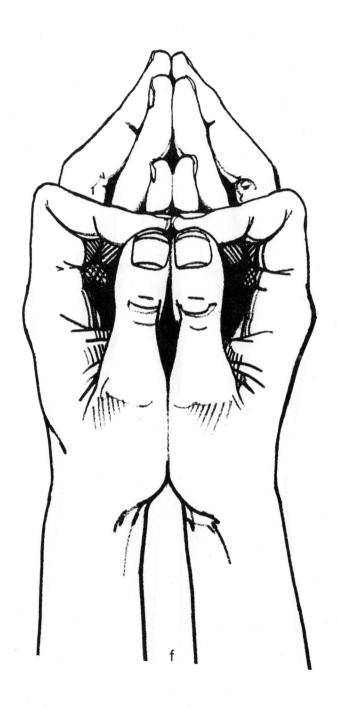

f

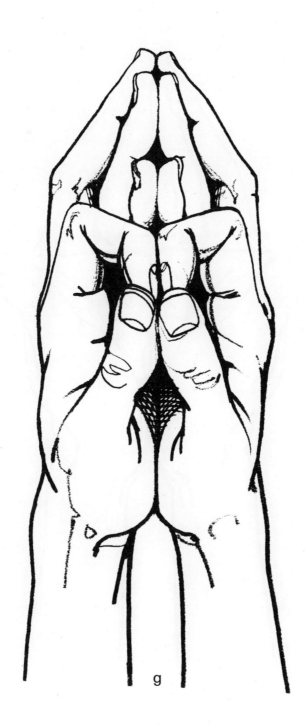

g

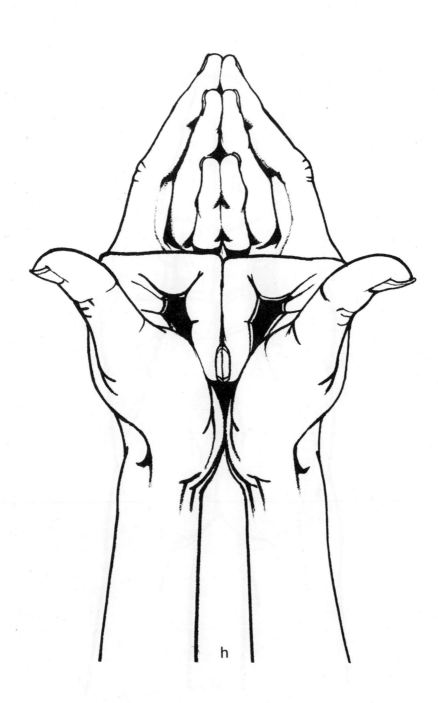

h

Esthetics 3

"Hand dancing"

Rhythm: (movement follows little finger) 1 (a–c), 2 (d–f), 3 (g), 4 (h)
stop, then (movement follows thumb) 1 (h–g), 2 (f–e), 3 (d–b), 4 (a)
stop; repeat continuously

Tempo: comfortable (above all, regular)

Duration: unlimited

NOTES:

The art of communicating by means of gestures is most highly developed in
the dance traditions of India and Indonesia. Anyone interested in exploring
the more subtle possiblilities of self-expression may benefit from studying
these more than 500 "mudras." (Contact the Hand Dynamics Institute for a
list of audio-visual material)

Related exercises:
Condition training—arms (see NOTES)

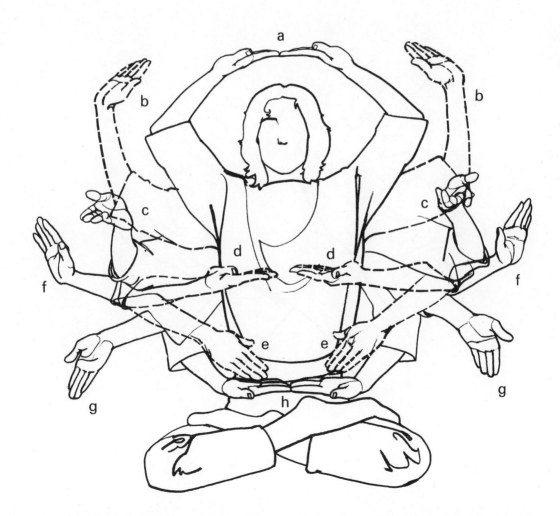

Psychophysical Balance

Psychophysical balance 1

Transferring the focal point of awareness from the thumb to the little finger
a. Starting position: little fingers clasp each other (left above right hand)
First, ±30 undulations towards the thumb, then ±30 undulations towards the little finger
b. Right above left hand (apart from that, the same)
Tempo: 2 undulations per sec (or slower)
Important: whenever you focus your awareness upon the little finger you will find that this has a subtlety-inducing effect upon both your macro- and micro-movements

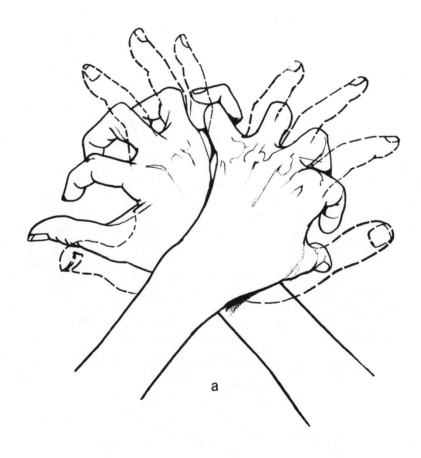

a

Psychophysical balance 2

a. Starting position: hands resting in your lap, thumbs clasp each other
   The movements of the fingers co-ordinate into a kind of "winging"
   (engaging middle and nail joints)
b. "Winging movement" extends to the whole finger (engaging palm,
   middle and nail joints), hands slowly rise to chest level

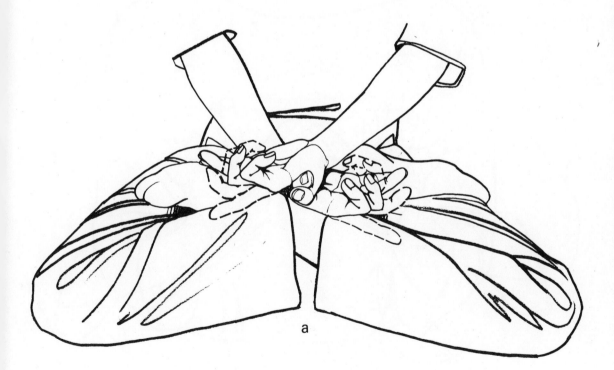

a

   c. Thumbs disengage (left hand slowly moves to the right, right hand to the left, both hands continue "winging")

d–h. "Winging movement" extends to the wrist joints (like d–h in Condition training—hands 10, except now "winging")

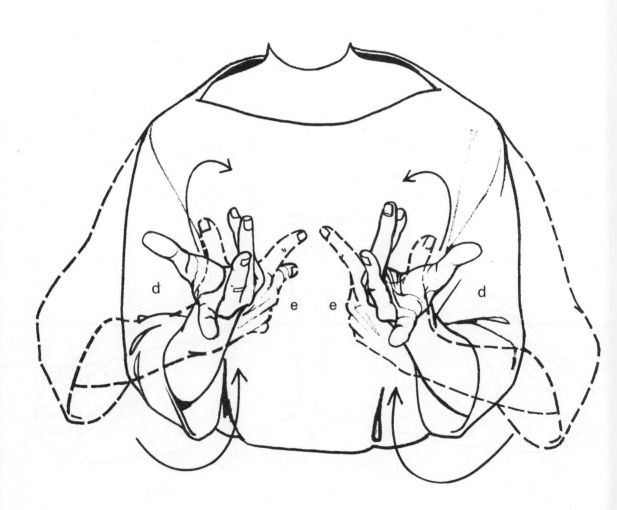

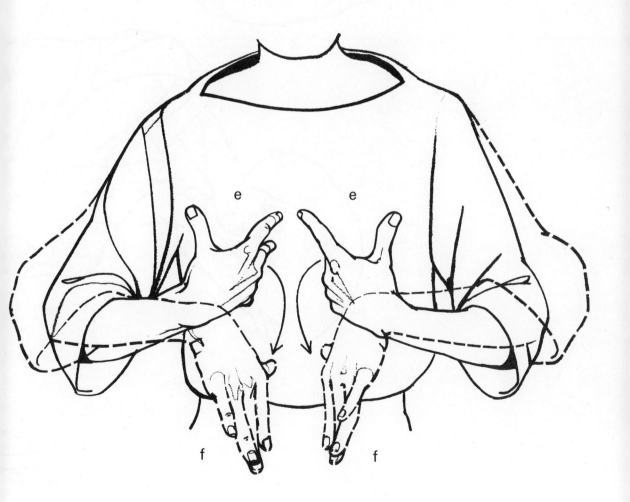

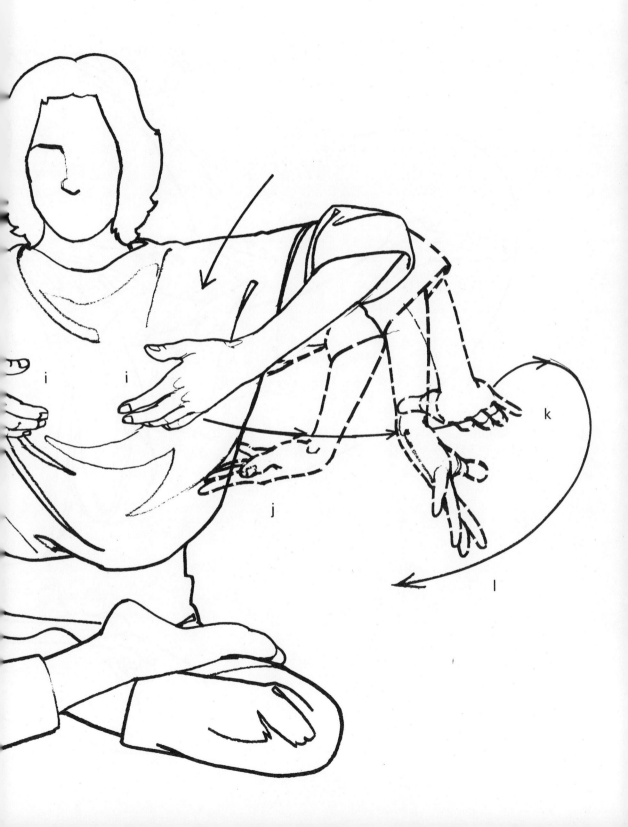

i–p. "Winging figure 8 movement" extends to lower and upper arms

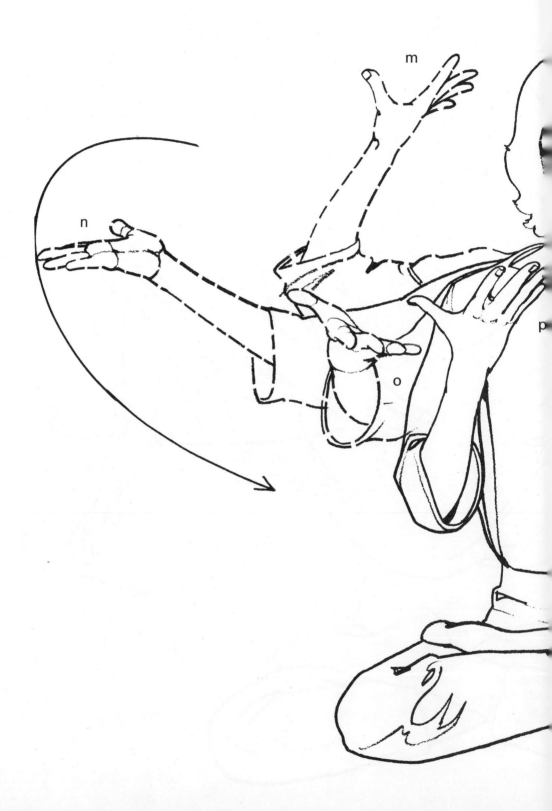

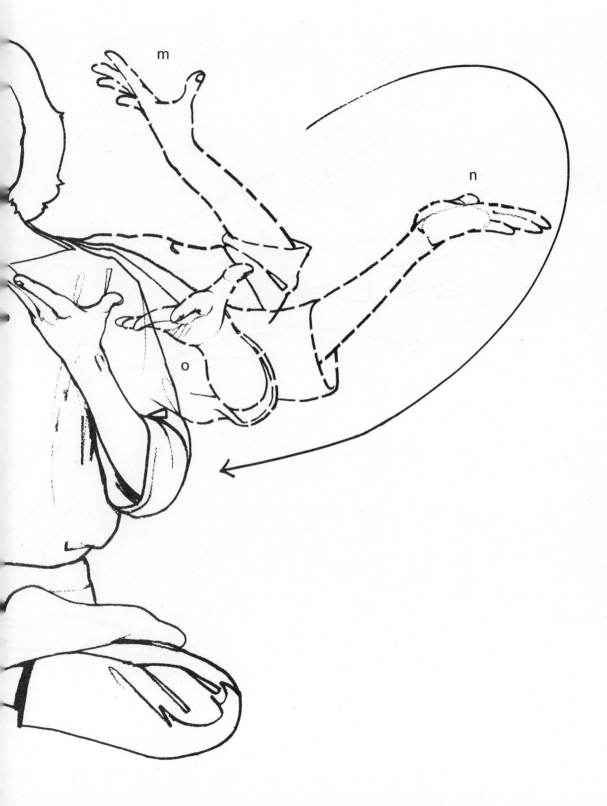

q–s. Upper arms remain horizontal, while the "winging figure 8 movement" is being transferred sideways

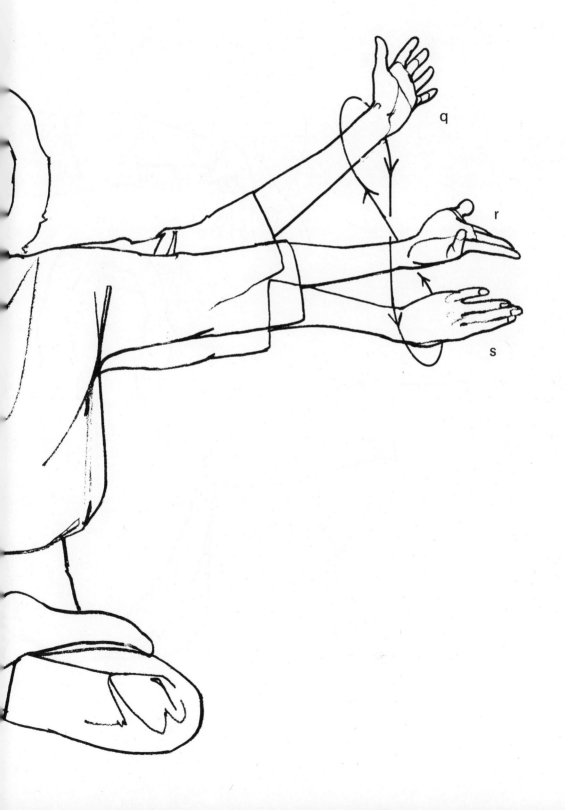

t. Upper and lower arms remain horizontally stretched, while the "winging figure 8 movement" is being transferred to the wrist

u. "Winging figure 8 movement" slows down until the hands come to a standstill ("gliding position")

v. Hands are "gliding" back into your lap . . . relax and enjoy the feeling
of being "uplifted"
Rhythm: fingers 5–4–3–2 (–1) stop, then 5–4–3–2 (–1) stop, then repeat
continuously
Tempo: slow (above all, comfortable)
Duration: 2 min (or longer)
Important: direction of movement follows the little finger
Tip: close your eyes and visualize the "flying" as well as the "gliding";
let your breathing during i–p undulate synchronously (hands above
arms: inhalation, hands below arms: exhalation)

Psychophysical balance 3

Harmony of movement
a. Body, mind and psyche: let it all FLOW
b. Gradually slow down your movements
c. Come to a standstill (remain ±15 sec in this sculpture-like body position)
d. Gradually accelerate your movements
e. Return to a "normal" pattern of behavior (without losing your newly acquired sense of harmony)
   Duration: 2–3 min (or longer)
f. Starting position: standing or kneeling breathing deeply and regularly, hands and arms move freely
   Tempo: extremely slow (½″–2″ per sec)
   Duration: unlimited
   Tip: imagine yourself to be a "celestial body" floating in space (become aware of the billions of stars surrounding you on all sides: above, below, right, left, in front and behind)
g. End f by turning little circles with: first the whole arm (in hanging position), then the lower arms only, then the hands only, then the fingers only (with attention focused upon fingertips), then relax (by letting hands and arms become very "heavy")
   Tempo: extremely slow
   Duration: 1–2 min

NOTES:
Balanced action is the result of a "meta-balance" between will, intellect, feeling and perception.
The will must be geared to applying the principle of harmony in daily life.
The intellect must be directed toward synthesis, that is to say, it must focus more on laws, relations and processes than on objects, forms and substances.
Feeling must rise above the level of instinct in order to act as a medium for relaying intuition.
Perception must have "depth" to it, that is to say, it should not remain tied-up to an automatized scanning of surfaces but instead, penetrate right into the heart of things.
Finally, no matter what action you undertake, be conscious of the fact that it is the Universe, the All-One transforming Itself through you!

Self-realization through self-observation:

a. Analyze your actions in terms of energy ("how" does "what" vibrate when I am working, playing, creating, communicating, relaxing making love, etc.?)

b. Observe your actions from a transpersonal perspective (what am "I" doing consciously? what am "I" doing unconsciously? what is being done to "me" and/or through "me"?)

c. Become more aware of your movements by experiencing them in slow motion (try not to look at them as relatively unimportant means to an "all-that-counts goal," but rather as indispensable links in an infinite chain of reality-constituting processes).

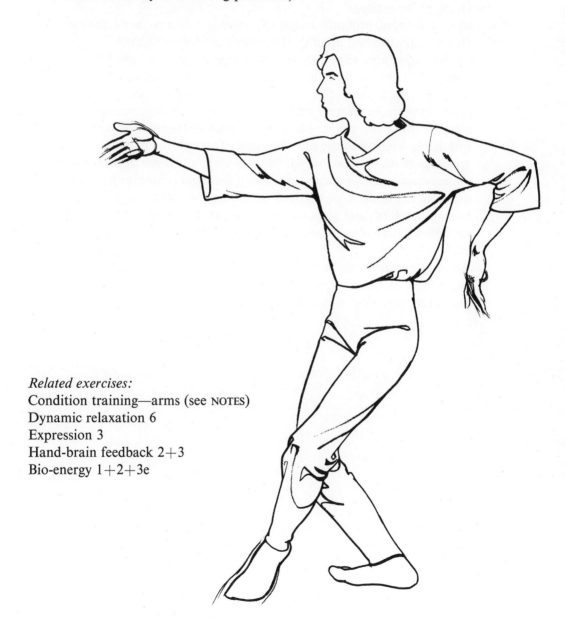

Related exercises:
Condition training—arms (see NOTES)
Dynamic relaxation 6
Expression 3
Hand-brain feedback 2+3
Bio-energy 1+2+3e

Hand-Brain Feedback

Hand-brain feedback 1

      Visualization exercise
      Starting position: relax the body (sitting or lying)
a.   Hands $\pm 6''$ from the eyes, observe both hands as precisely as possible (register each detail)
      Duration: unlimited
b.   Close your eyes, bring the hands to a resting position, then visualize a.
c.   Direct your attention upon the little finger of the right hand
      Let the little finger engage in an inner monologue about itself (for example: "I am the little finger of the right hand. I consist of three moving parts: a palm joint, a middle joint and a nail joint. On the places most prone to wear and tear, the skin, my protective shield, is buffered with extra callus. The host of touch receptors I am surrounded with is my window to the outside world. Through the muscular system, my range of activity extends all the way up to the lower arm. Through the nervous system, I am wired up with the hand center in the cortical region of the brain. I am pledged to serving the organism, which brought me forth and gives me nourishment. I am collaborating with my fellow extremities for the sake of realizing life's inborn aspirations, etc.)
      Accompany each statement with an appropriate visualization
      Important: do the same with all other parts of the hand (and the body), but never more than one monologue at a time

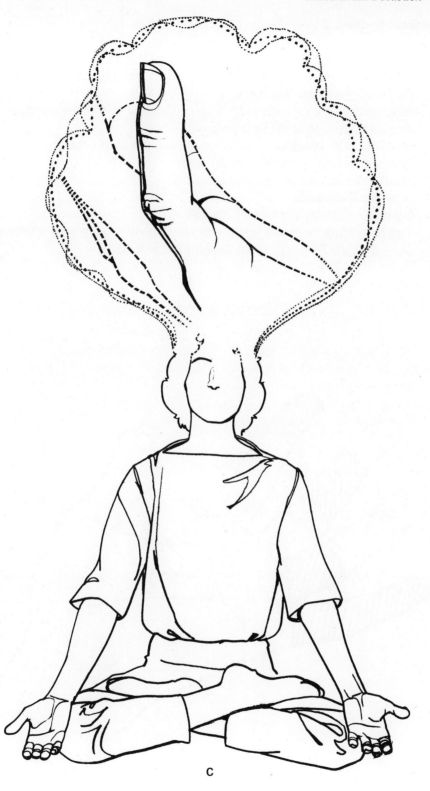

c

Hand-brain feedback 2

Starting position: close your eyes, hands and fingers co-ordinate into a undulating figure 8 motion (like in Condition training—hands 10 d–i)
Direct all your attention upon:

a. First the thumbs, then the index fingers, then the middle fingers, then the ring-fingers, then the little fingers
b. Next, the palm phalanxes one by one, starting with the thumb
c. Then the middle phalanxes, one by one
d. Finally, the nail phalanxes, one by one
   Tempo: comfortable
   Duration: ±10 sec per unit of exercise
   Tip: for adding more subtlety to everyday activities, keep your attention upon the little fingers (plus all fingertips, if you can)

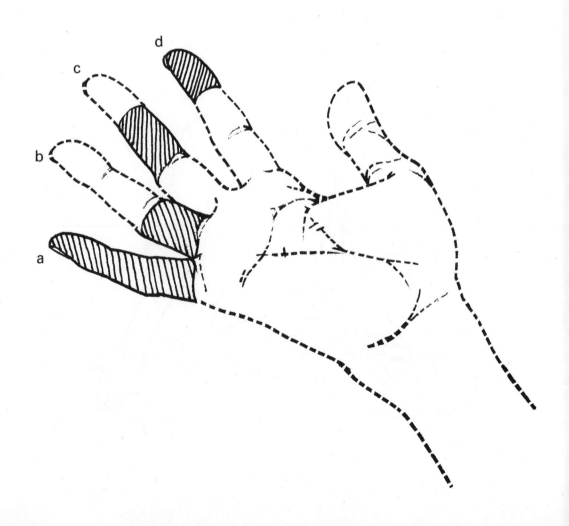

Hand-brain feedback 3

Selective stimulation of brain hemispheres
a. Stimulation of the right brain
Starting position: the right part of the body is resting on a bed, right palm on back of the head, the left arm and leg are hanging alongside the bed
After 3–5 min of total relaxation: eyes are turned as far left as possible (very important), and the whole left part of the body starts to move (arm, hand, fingers, leg, foot, toes, all at once), while the right part of the body remains relaxed
b. Stimulation of the left brain (the same as in a., but in reversed position)
Tempo: comfortable
Duration: 3–5 min per brain hemisphere or longer (for an extra strong effect)
Tip: if the leg becomes tired, the stimulation can be continued by means of the hand-arm system only (don't forget to keep your eyes "cornered")
If there is no bed available, you may follow the same procedure while lying on your side (somewhat more tiring, yet equally effective)
Explanation: The right brain specializes in "non-verbal" modes of organizing reality. It is more oriented toward situations than details and functions predominantly on the basis of feeling. Its strength lies in the ability to think in images and sounds. Those who need to develop creativity and intuition (and/or ambidexterity) will choose to stimulate this side of the brain in particular.
The left brain specializes in rational-analytical modes of organizing reality. It is more oriented toward details than situations and functions predominantly on the basis of intellect. Its strength lies in the ability to think in words, numbers and abstractions.
Those who need to develop efficiency, discipline and cool-headedness will choose to stimulate this side of the brain in particular.
The central idea behind this exercise is to provide a tool for balancing the complementary opposites within ourselves. Those who want to experiment with it more extensively should first read some popular books on brain research (see for instance, *The Right Brain* by Thomas R. Blakeslee or *The Psychology of Consciousness* by Robert Ornstein or *The Brain Revolution* by Marilyn Ferguson)

Related exercises:
Condition training—arms (see NOTES)
Micro-precision 2+3
Dynamic relaxation 6
Psychophysical balance 3

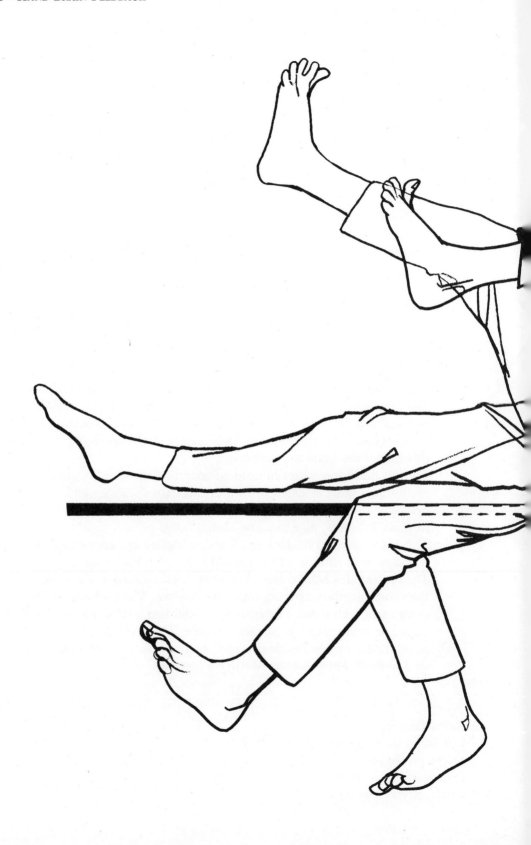

Bio-Energy

Bio-energy 1

Perceiving bio-energy
Close your eyes: visualize the body as a "bio-magnetic" force field
(left side of the body=negative pole, right side of the body=positive
pole)
a. "Backs" facing each other (±20 sec)

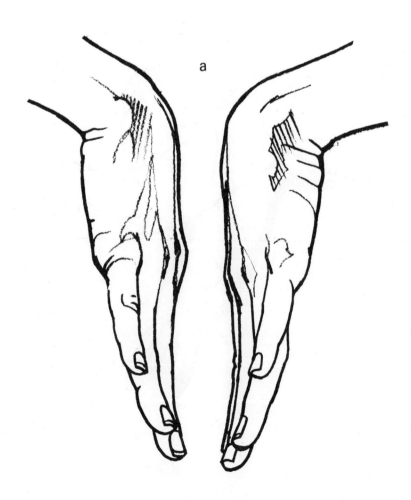

b. Palms facing each other ($\pm$20 sec)
   a+b ... altogether 3 times
   Important: in case you feel an "invisible cushion" between your hands,
   don't be startled; it just means, that you have come "in touch" with
   the energy dimension of yourself

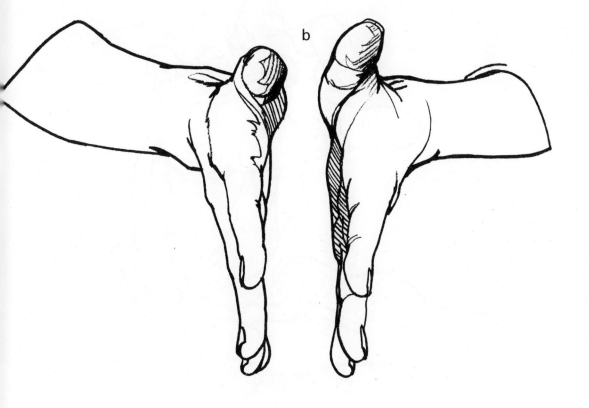

b

Bio-energy 2

Generating bio-energy
a. Let the left hand move around the right hand (in a half circle, palm facing palm, then palm facing "back" ... repeat continuously)
Rhythm: downwards ±1 sec, upwards ±1 sec; repeat continuously
Duration: 40–60 sec
Important: feel as if you are "rubbing up" a continuously growing "ball of energy"
b. Transfer the "ball of energy" to the left hand, then "rub it up" with your right hand
c. Let the "ball of energy" grow bigger and bigger until your entire body is encompassed by it
Tip: channel this surplus flow of energy into your perceptions, feelings, thoughts and actions

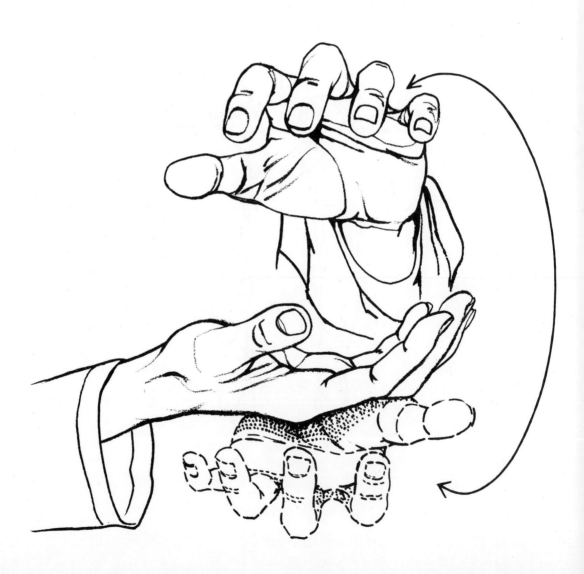

Bio-energy 3

Projecting bio-energy
Imagine that through your fingertips "laser-like beams" are shooting
into infinite space

a. Imagine that these infinitely elongated fingers are scanning remote
objects
b. Imagine that these elongated fingers are beaming right through the walls
c. Direct the "beams" of the one hand on the palm of the other (feel
the actual transfer of energy)
d. Especially during meditative dancing, feel how your "elongated fingers"
generate a vortex in the invisible world of energy
Tempo: stately
Duration: unlimited

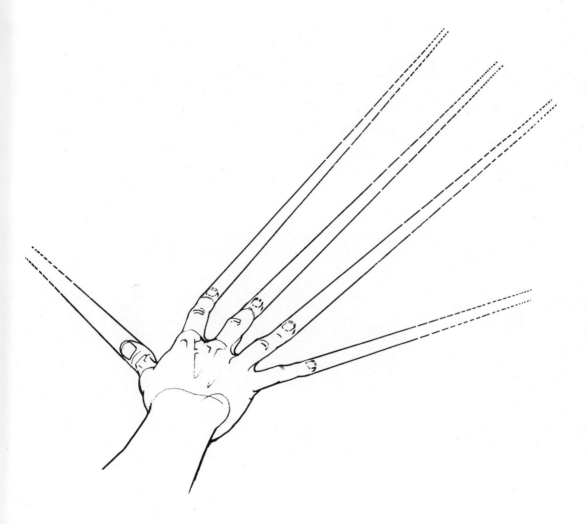

NOTES:
Try the following:
One person is lying on his stomach.
A second person uses his left (and/or right) hand as a sensor to detect different vibratory qualities above different parts of the body (let your hands be "carried" by the energy field of your partner).
Change positions after about 10 or 15 min.

Related exercises:
Sensitivity 4
Dynamic relaxation 6
Passive relaxation 1+2+3
Psychophysical balance 2+3
Hand-brain feedback 3

Bibliography

Physiology of the hand

Kapandji, I.A., *The Physiology of the Joints*, Vol. I, "Upper Limb," Churchill Livingstone, Edinburgh, London and New York, 1970.
Mesker, Dr. P., *De Menselijke Hand*, Dekker en Van de Degt, Nijmegen, 1980.

Sense of touch

Montagu, Ashley, *Touching: The Human Significance of the Skin*, Colombia University Press, New York, 1971.
Hardison, J., *Let's Touch: How and why to do it*, Prentice-Hall Inc., Englewood Cliffs, 1980.

Hand-brain relations

Blakeslee, T. R., *The Right Brain: A new understanding of the unconscious mind and its creative powers*, Anchor Press/ Doubleday, 1980.
Ornstein, R., *The Psychology of Consciousness*, Penguin, 1972.
Ferguson, Marilyn, *The Brain Revolution*, Taplinger, New York 1973.
Edwards, Betty, *Drawing on the Right Side of the Brain: A course in enhancing creativity and artistic confidence*, J.P. Tarcher Inc., Los Angeles, 1979.

Psychology of gestures

Lee, L. & Charlton, J., *The Hand Book: Interpreting handshakes, gestures, power signals and sexual signs*, Prentice-Hall Inc., Englewood Cliffs, 1980.
Morris D., *Gestures: their origin and distribution*, Cape, London, 1979.
Kiener, F., *Hand, Gebärde und Charakter*, München, 1962.
Stangl, A., *Die Sprache des Körpers*, Econ Verlag, Düsseldorf, 1977.

Philosophy of the hand

Napier, J. R., *Hands*, George Allen & Unwin, London, 1980.
Sorell, W., *The Story of the Human Hand*, Weidenfeld and Nicholson, London, 1968.
Hessenbruch, H., *Die Umfassende Bedeutung der Hände*, Verlage der Lebensschule, Unterlängenhardt, 1971.
Révész, G., *De Menselijke Hand*, Nord-Hollandsche Uitgevers Mij., Amsterdam, 1941.

Paranormal hand functions

Carter, Mildred, *Hand Reflexology*, Parker Publishing Company, Inc., West Nyack, New York, 1975.

Blate, Michael, *How to Heal Yourself Using Hand Acupressure* (*Hand Reflexology*), Falkynor Books, Davie, 1983

Krieger, Dolores, *Therapeutic Touch: How to use your hands to help or to heal*, Prentice-Hall Inc., Englewood Cliffs, 1979.

Gordon, Richard, *Your Healing Hands*, *The Polarity Experience*, Unity Press, Santa Cruz, 1978.

Gunther, Bernhard, *Energy, Ecstasy and Your Seven Vital Chakras*, Aquarian Publishing Company, Wellingborough, 1979.

Joy, Brugh, M.D., *Joy's Way: An Introduction to the Potentials for Healing with Body Energies*, J.P. Tarcher Inc, Los Angeles, 1979.

Middendorf, Ilse (edited by Gerald Kogan, Ph. D.), *Your Body Works: A guide to health, energy and balance*, Transformations Press, Berkeley, 1980.

Finger games for children

Baur, A., *Das Fingertheater*, Novalis Verlag, Schaffhausen, 1974.

Baur, A., *Die Finger Tanzen*, Novalis Verlag, Schaffhausen, 1981.

Related topics

Chirology & Chiromancy
Graphology & Graphotherapy
Hand Massage
Movement therapy
"Touch for Health"
Sign language
Mudras
Handicraft
Physical training for instrumentalists
Karma Yoga (Vita Activa)